An Unassum

The Making of the
Bedfordshire Countryside

Brian Kerr

An Unassuming County:

The Making of the Bedfordshire Countryside

Brian Kerr

EVENTISPRESS

First published in Great Britain in 2014

by EVENTISPRESS

A catalogue record for this book is available from the British Library.

ISBN 978-0-9572520-9-7

Printed by Berforts Information Press
Stevenage

DEDICATION

To soil surveyors everywhere who try to make sense of what is below their feet.

PREFACE

The idea of writing a brief and user-friendly guide which describes the landscape in Bedfordshire has been with me for some time; in fact, since my family moved to the county in 1982. The move to the lowlands of England from the uplands of Scotland meant that my family left behind the well-loved hills of Galloway and swapped them for the less dramatic landscapes of the clay vales of Bedfordshire. During that move, a less than encouraging friend from Yorkshire described the county as 'flat and soggy and smelling of Brussels sprouts'. In an effort to prove him wrong and get to know Bedfordshire better, I have walked with my family in many parts of the county for over a decade. However, only recently, when I began to walk regularly with a ramblers group, did the idea of some form of introductory guide take shape.

One motive for this endeavour was to encourage all countryside users, especially the growing number of ramblers, to use their eyes more keenly and try to appreciate the countryside more by asking questions about the landscapes they are walking through. The idea is to encourage countryside users to look beyond the merely picturesque. What stone is this church built from? How old is this woodland? Can the pattern of the fields be explained? Why are there ridges and swales in the fields? Some of these questions are discussed in this text, and I hope that more people will be stimulated to be curious and that walkers, cyclists and general observers of the great outdoors will become more informed about the fascinating and attractive county of Bedfordshire. Our idealised impressions of the countryside are in part moulded by landscape painters. Constable, perhaps the greatest of the English landscape artists, was aware of this when he wrote that 'we see nothing till we truly understand it'. It is in this spirit of understanding that this text attempts to provide some insights.

This may not at the outset seem like an easy or interesting prospect. Bedfordshire, as remarked on by my Yorkshire friend, does not have a great national following as one of England's most attractive counties. The charm of the Devon lanes, the drama of the Cornish coast or the wildness of the Northumberland moorland would be difficult to match in Bedfordshire. This sentiment was echoed by one of the first agricultural surveyors working in the county in the early nineteenth century who described Bedfordshire as 'an unassuming county', which has been adopted in the title of this volume. In a book first published in 1977 entitled *Landscapes of Britain,* Bedfordshire is only mentioned once, and only then to illustrate derelict land illustrated by dismal pictures of clay pits and failed restoration in Marston Vale. In a more recent publication, *A History of England in 100 Places,* not one was in Bedfordshire. Unfortunately, that is an image problem the county has lived with for some time. Bedfordshire was often seen as a county to travel through rather than explore.

In contrast, anyone who has taken the trouble to explore even a little within Bedfordshire could argue for a favourite walk or view. This book takes the view that all the landscapes within the county have something to offer and are worth visiting with an open mind. This guide provides a key to unlock some of the clues that explain how the landscapes have come to look as they are. This includes the fundamental part played by basic geology, processes such as ice and glaciations, the use made of the resources by man since the earliest times, and finally the most recent pressures and changes now facing the county, which are tackled in an easily understood way. The approach I have taken has been to subdivide the area of Bedfordshire into five distinct landscapes, based mostly on geology. This then separates at a basic level the clear differences between, for example, the chalk downs and the clay vales. This guide then attempts to explain the more subtle differences in the landscape, which are already understood by farmers and gardeners but may not be so clear on the ground. The work of the glacial ice that covered the country in the most recent geological period (by 12,000 years before present (BP) the majority of England was ice free) has led to variations which are important in how the land is used but may not be striking in any topographical way. For example, the importance of the alluvial terraces of the Ouse Valley, valued since Roman times for fruit and vegetable production, or the former peat workings of Flitvale, may have no dramatic landscape features but are very important to those who work the land.

A personal interest in the mapping and recording of soil patterns and their use in the UK and elsewhere has led to an approach in this text which emphasises soil changes across the landscape and how they have influenced land use. The more technical aspects of this are explored in Chapter 8, and the text can be used and enjoyed without struggling to understand technical language. However, it is important to explain something of the soil pattern in Bedfordshire, as this veneer of soils is responsible for so much of what we see and how we use the land. This is not often obvious, but playing golf or horse riding or cycling on the sandy tracts of the Greensand Ridge, which forms a striking feature through the heart of the county, is possible in winter, when the lowland clays are sodden. In the same way, building a road through the chalk cutting on the approach to Luton Airport requires different costings and techniques to the skills needed to ensure a solid road foundation across the peat in the valley of the River Flit.

In bringing together this guide I have drawn on and acknowledged the work of many others who have, in the past, studied various aspects of the county. This includes early geological mapping and soil maps created as far back as 1860s. Writing about the history of the landscape in England is dangerous, as so many disciplines have made contributions to our understanding. Geology, climate studies, archaeology, agricultural history and many more areas of science have added insights into how the landscape has been shaped. However, in an increasingly specialist world, weaving all these strands together is a useful exercise: it has certainly been an absorbing challenge.

An important influence in explaining the historical evolution of the countryside has been Peter Bigmore's landmark text, *The Bedfordshire and Huntingdonshire Landscape,* on the making of the English landscape. This book has been a constant source of reference and inspiration to me. The scholarly work of Joyce Godber, who held the post of county archivist for 20 years, has been a fruitful source. Her 1984 publication, *History of Bedfordshire 1066–1888,* contains detailed information on land administration and ownership.

At a more general level, two outstanding academic works have provided inspiration. W. G. Hoskins' *The Making of the English Landscape* provided early clues on reading a landscape, and in a later volume entitled *English Landscapes* the author develops the twin themes: that everything in the countryside is older than we think, and the complementary idea that continuity is the most important aspect of the English landscape. These ideas have been echoed in this guide. The work of Oliver Rackham in *The History of the Countryside* also gave me a direct push to completing this book. Rackham, like many other authors, does not spend much time in Bedfordshire but, in his preface, points out that any perceived unfairness in his text is best addressed by the reader writing his own book. I have taken him at his word.

Table of contents

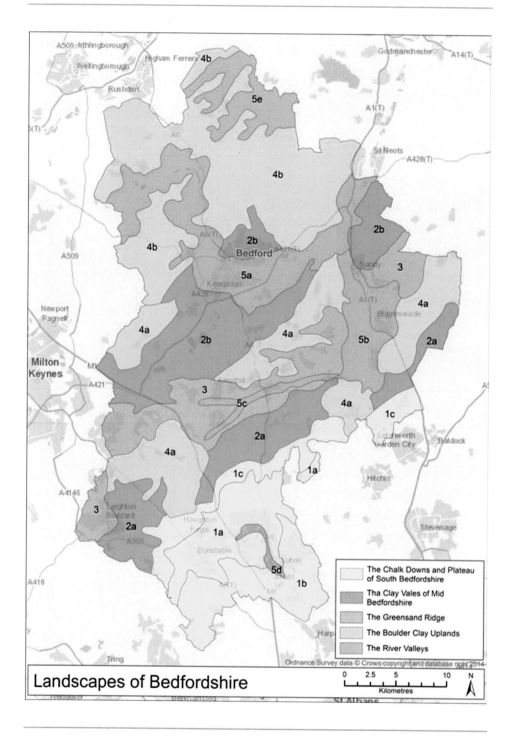

Landscapes of Bedfordshire

The Chalk Downs and Plateau of South Bedfordshire

Tha Clay Vales of Mid Bedfordshire

The Greensand Ridge

The Boulder Clay Uplands

The River Valleys

Ordnance Survey data © Crown copyright and database right 2014

0   2.5   5   10   N
Kilometres

CHAPTER 1

THE BEDFORDSHIRE LANDSCAPE

The Marston Vale from the edge of the Greensand Ridge

This chapter title is unashamedly modelled on a well-known book entitled *The Making of the English Landscape*, by W. G. Hoskins, which was first published in 1955. In this text he describes, in a masterful way, the evolution of the landscapes of England and acknowledges the work of geologists in setting the scene for understanding later historical landscape changes. Hoskins approached landscape like a narrative, as a visible record of what has gone before. Once you know how to read it, then patterns are discernible and clues to the historical use of the land can be unravelled. He also provides a powerful analogy in describing the geological formation as the bones of the landscape and explains that, beyond a certain point, the historian is required to take this fundamental structure and add the flesh needed to cover the skeleton. This contributes the detail and texture to the landscape as we see it today.

In this guide I have added a third dimension. I would argue that the flesh on the geological landscape skeleton is the soils that cover the solid rocks and deep clays. These influenced strongly how land was used in the past and, most importantly, impact on what we see today. The soils below our feet have exerted a powerful force on how land is farmed, what is grown, where we build, or how the land is otherwise used. Bedfordshire, in fact, is an excellent example of soil cover influencing the landscape pattern, as the clay vales and the adjacent upland ridges that mark the undulating topography respond differently to drainage, cultivation, grazing or forestry. Soil therefore directly impacts on how landowners and managers use land today for production and recreation. These soils, often developed within material deposited by the last glaciers to cover southern England, are therefore akin to the flesh that smooths out the geological bones and shape the landscape in which we walk, build, farm or garden.

The most visible and impressive element in the landscape is of course the impact made by man. The view of the post-Second World War brick-making smoke stacks at Marston Vale and the great voids of the clay pits adjacent are obvious examples. However, there are many less immediate landscape elements that contribute to the landscape history. These range from the subtle field patterns which date from the colonisation and farming by settlers during the time of the Romans, to the large-scale enclosures of the open fields in the eighteenth and nineteenth centuries. Each of these many changes has made a distinct – but sometimes not immediately obvious – impression on the landscape within the county.

The Geological Skeleton of the County

There are already many good accounts of the geology of Bedfordshire. One account summarises the geology neatly and explains the ridge and vale landscape thus:

'To drive north through Bedfordshire is to drive back in time. The chalk to the south is younger than the adjacent Gault Clay, which is younger than the Lower Greensand of the central ridge, [which is] in turn younger than the Oxford Clay and the Great Oolitic Limestone on the northern plateau.'

In other words, the rocks are older in the north than in the south. Whatever the age, the landscape of today carries the imprint of the underlying geology: the impact of geological history is all around us, from the brick pits in the Oxford Clay to the recreation areas of the chalk downs above Dunstable. There are, of course, many minor variations in this pattern. The sand pits and Fuller's Earth extractions on the Greensand are now being reclaimed and the Ouse Valley gravel pits are being turned into wildfowl reserves and, perhaps in future, a rowing lake. The architecture of the county has been heavily influenced by its geology. The remarkable parish churches are often built in the fragile Greensand stone – and, in north Bedfordshire, of limestone, which is the common building stone in villages such as Pavenham and was also used in the Felmersham bridge.

However, it is through the geological influence on soils, and therefore on agriculture, that the landscape and character of the county have been directly shaped, and this is explained in the next section. A more detailed explanation of the influence of the geology on the flora of the county has recently been given in *The Flora of Bedfordshire* (C. R. Boon and A. R. Outen, 2011). In this book the authors note that the link between the geology, the soils and the flora is being irrevocably changed in many parts of Bedfordshire, and appeal for an improved understanding and appreciation of the need to conserve ecosystems as a whole.

The geological formations that are represented in the county are illustrated on the geological map in Chapter 2, which is produced with acknowledgement to the former Bedfordshire County Council. In addition, a section of the geological table is reproduced, showing the relationship between all the formations mentioned, and including some brief notes on each.

The Soil Cover

Throughout this volume there are references to the ways in which agriculture, forestry and other land use are related to the soil. This emphasis reflects not only a personal bias but also the importance of what is below our feet in any explanation of how the landscape and scenery we see today have been formed. One of the fascinating things about the county is the extreme variations in soil conditions over relatively short distances. An account of the agriculture by Thomas Stone, writing in 1794, illustrates this:

'Every soil and every mixture of soil commonly seen on high land in the United Kingdom may be found in this county, from the strongest clay to the lightest sand. The various kinds of soil are frequently found in small patterns and so much surrounded and intermixed with each other that no very accurate delineation of these can be made.'

Despite reservations on the complexity, there are several maps of the soils of Bedfordshire, and these are discussed in Chapter 8.

However, it is not necessary to be a scientist – only a gardener – to quickly realise that Bedfordshire is a county dominated by clays. Using the criteria adopted by the Soil Survey of England and Wales, almost two-thirds of all the land in Bedfordshire is classified as having soils with impeded drainage – usually on clays. The brick-making Oxford Clay of Marston Vale is better known than the Gault Clay deposits north of Barton-le-Clay, which are also used for brick manufacture. However, even on the chalk south of Luton the 'clay with flints' provides a stiff and tenacious soil, as does the glacial till (previously referred to as boulder clay) deposited by ice in the north and centre of the county; around Cranfield, for example. Some Bedfordshire clay deposits even enter the geological record in a formal way: the Ampthill Clay is a recognised geological term, despite the town usually being associated with the sandy nature of the Greensand Ridge.

Throughout Britain soil conditions were one of the factors that influenced the early settlers. Soils that are free-draining, with a loamy texture, and not excessively acid, encourage a wide range of plants, including nutritious grasses and clovers, and were valued by early livestock keepers. These became important for grazing animals, which in turn fertilised the soil. In Bedfordshire the importance of the freely drained soils to be found on the river terraces and on the Greensand Ridge, which tend to be warmer in spring than the adjacent cold and imperfectly drained clays, were also of great interest to both the cultivator and pastoralist. As cultivation expanded these loamy soils became an important settlement factor, and Anglo- Saxon farmers turned to the finer-textured soils, which are inherently more fertile than the lighter more sandy soils preferred by the early settlers. In the county the loams and marls at the bottom of the scarps, such as along the chalk edge, were favoured. A first-century plough – an 'ard' – recovered from gravel workings at Odell and conserved in Bedford Museum illustrates the arrival of farmers practising settled agriculture on the more favourable soils.

Much later, with the appearance of wheeled ploughs, the colder and heavy clay soil could be tackled. This resulted in the *ridge and furrow* relic landscape which is so characteristic of Bedfordshire and the English Midlands in general. The assumption is that this dates from the open field systems of the eleventh to fourteenth centuries. Most of this ridge and furrow landscape has now been ploughed out using the modern deep tillage tackle pulled by powerful tractors: the best examples remaining are on old or permanent pasture associated with poorly drained soils. The clay vales with inherently fertile soils only became important when tile drainage was laid by an army of labourers in the nineteenth century, followed by the use of steam ploughs and, later still, the low-pressure tyres fitted to multi-horsepower tractors with hydraulic linkages to huge ploughs. The result is now a workable *tilth* on the heaviest soils if field operations are undertaken when conditions are not too wet or too dry.

The interaction of farmers with their soils is a two-way process. It is evident that the soils deeply influenced settlement and farming methods, but the reverse is also true. The drainage of the clays is only one example of how man has altered the soils he farms: since much of Bedfordshire's arable land is clay, the under-drainage of these soils made arable farming possible.

Ridge and Furrow: The Shadow of the Plough

Often glimpsed from a train window or when walking across old pasture land, ridge and furrow is the pattern of parallel ridges created by previous ploughing in large open fields. This mode of arable farming was common across England from the Roman period to the end of the seventeenth century. Much of the older pasture in the English Midlands is rippled by closely spaced ridges and furrows, which are formed by the use of a plough on the same strip of land each year, with the ploughman and his team moving in a clockwise direction, working a long but narrow strip of land. As the plough could not be reversed, the soil was moved to the right each time, eventually forming a ridge.

The Agricultural Heritage as a Historical Record

This brief guide is not intended to provide a comprehensive or academic history of the landscape of Bedfordshire, but to make any visit to the countryside more informed. The best history of the evolution of our modern landscape remains Peter Bigmore's 1979 book, *The Bedfordshire and Huntingdonshire Landscape*. The approach in this book has been to take the physical landscapes of Bedfordshire and try to unravel why each has a distinctive pattern of agriculture and land use. The historical record for which documentation is available traces the influence of landowners and managers on the landscape, and it is at this time that the most striking changes come about. However, the influence of the geology and soils on the land is usually clear, and the sympathetic use of land in harmony with environmental limitations always makes good business and economic sense.

So, while the striking features of the Marston Clay Vale remain the residue of the brick industry, the surrounding arable fields can be cropped thanks to the efforts of the army of drainage workers who have converted these wet, intractable soils into land which can now be productively used. It made economic sense to drain these flat and fertile fields and manage their use carefully for arable grain production.

Modern tractor and implements working on chalk soils in the east of the county

Using landscape histories such as that written by Peter Bigmore, it is possible to describe the evolution of the landscape in a number of broad phases, each of which has left a distinctive imprint on what we see. These historical periods, when the pattern of the landscape changed markedly, are described briefly below. Each phase grades imperceptibly into the next and there are no clear time horizons: change has been influenced by climate, available technology, social movements, economics and – not least – fashion.

The Earliest Settlers

Napoleon is reported to have said, 'geography explains history', and in Bedfordshire the routes used by the earliest settlers illustrate this well, the best example being the Icknield Way, which cuts diagonally across the county, following the chalk scarp from east to west. The views from the high points of the Way, now a long-distance footpath, give excellent views of the Gault Clay agricultural plain to the north and east across Bedfordshire (Chapter 10 has a more detailed description of this well-used pathway). This vale would have been heavily wooded and almost impenetrable to pre-Iron Age settlers, whereas the chalk would have been more lightly wooded and easily cleared. The importance of this dry, upland chalk route into the interior of Britain cannot be underestimated, giving access from the coast and avoiding the wet and ill-drained lowlands. The Icknield Way is one of the most ancient routes in the country and is certainly pre-Roman, but its exact chronology is uncertain. The best history of this ancient trackway can be found in Edward Thomas's account, *The Ickneild Way,* [1] first published in 1911.

The beginning of land clearance and the shaping of the landscape to serve agriculture seems to have begun in the fourth millennium BC. Palaeolithic stone axes are recorded from Caddington, near Luton, and two stone axes both crafted from rock found in Cornwall have been located in Ampthill and Wyboston, providing evidence of long-distance trade into and through the county. Actual evidence from the county is not plentiful, but the dating of sites on the chalk of East Anglia and the Chilterns has noted a reduction in the level of tree pollen and the rise in weed species, marking the clearance of land for grazing. By 1,500 BC grain seeds from a site on the Lower Chalk on the fringes of present-day Luton clearly signal the arrival of cultivation.
The clearance of the chalk uplands during this Bronze Age period was matched by changes in the lighter soils of the Greensand uplands, with heather species (as in the Breckland Heaths of East Anglia) taking over. Woodland that has been felled finds it difficult to re-establish without protection from grazing. The result is the lowland heather heaths, such as at Sandy, Ampthill and at Aspley Heath. Gradually other areas were being farmed, and on the edge of the Greensand at Salford an Iron Age village was occupied by 500 BC. At Haynes Hall there is pollen evidence of woodland clearance and shifting cultivation.

However, it required a long time span, to 500 AD, for any settlement to make an impact on the clay vales, with a settlement close to Stewartby being one example. In general, the landscape of Bedfordshire was only lightly touched by these Bronze Age peoples, and then only on the chalk and Greensand Ridges and on the river gravels of the Ouse and Ivel. What evidence we have is from gravel pits which have both thrown up prehistoric sites and also destroyed these in the process of extraction. In contrast, the forested clay lands were avoided by early farmers. The best evidence of agriculture is Iron Age field boundaries or banks, known as 'lynchets', on the chalk slopes close to Pegston.

---

[1].The spelling by Thomas is 'Ickneild'. The OS spelling is 'Icknield', which I have used here.

Farming on the Slope: Strip Lynchets on the Chalk

A distinctive feature of the steeply sloping chalk escarpment are banks or terraces which follow the contour and often occur on the more sheltered sides of valleys. In Bedfordshire, Pegsdon and Deacon Hills are good examples, as are sites north of Barton and Badgers Hill near Luton. These features are common on the shallow chalk soils and are created by ploughing on a hillside, thereby building a flatter area above, to be farmed as a terrace. Early farmers valued this chalk land, as it was easily cleared, but any advantage needed to be set against the difficulties of working on a slope and cultivating a shallow soil. The ridging and terracing of slopes was the answer, and also reduced the danger of soil erosion and land slippage. Archaeologists now believe that these are Iron Age farming relics with a possible early date of 800 BC, with sporadic working until the Middle Ages. The key features of these early 'field systems' are that they are in a strip, along the contour, and enclose a small, but precious, area of flatter land. Found throughout lowland England, usually on chalk, these fields have often been compared with the early square Celtic fields in the western counties.

Mixed woodland, which encourages thriving ground flora including this example at Maulden Woods with an attractive display of bluebells, is very characteristic of the Greensand Ridge

Roman Settlement in Bedfordshire

The Roman imprint on the landscape in Bedfordshire is relatively light. There are no large towns or extrovert villas such as those which are present in adjacent counties, and the most obvious feature is the military route of Watling Street, now the A5. However, this does not mean an absence of Roman influence, and there is evidence that the clay vales were being farmed for the first time using iron-clad ploughs. Roman settlement and Romano-British farmers still favoured the river gravels, which offered flat land close to the lines of communication with easily worked soils. Three localities on these gravels have been identified using air photographic evidence. Around Harrold and Odell the field pattern is claimed to be Romano-British, but this is difficult to determine on the ground. In the Ouse Valley close to Cople and Willington, downstream from Bedford, there is a similar pattern; and on the Ivel, in parishes such as Northill and Southill around Upper Caldecote, there are Romano-British settlements and some evidence of a field pattern that conforms to Roman dimensions. Further north the Roman imprint is much clearer, with the Nene Valley pottery industry now recognised by archaeologists as one of the major centres for pottery in eastern England: Roman records also show that the Nene Valley was a local centre of wine production – probably serving the garrison troops on Hadrian's Wall.

Bedfordshire at the Time of the Domesday Book

The county was well settled by the time of the Domesday Book of 1086. It was described by one commentator as 'well settled and a model agricultural county', and for some reason the Greensand areas were represented by pigs in the Bedfordshire record. The parish at Haynes had 500 pigs recorded, for example. A vineyard at Eaton Socon was noted and another monastery vineyard at Northill. There was a remarkably even spread of occupied settlements, with the lands of Dunstable Abbey carefully noted.

As medieval farming expanded, especially under the stewardship of monastic settlements such as that at Dunstable, open fields bounded by ancient hedges were cut directly from the woodland. Residual woodland remained as a resource open to all on higher or steeper land and formed an important part of livelihoods for the medieval population.

The management of woodland has left an interesting relic in some of our woods. The cutting of coppice, based on a 10- or 15-year cycle, using hazel, maple and ash and then allowing it to regenerate and produce woody stems to be used as poles, was common across lowland England. 'Coppice with standards' refers to the scattered oaks which were left to grow to maturity as 'standards' for use in construction. This system fell into disuse when intensive labour was required and the shadow of difficult times fell across the landscape.

The Plague and Deserted Settlements

Throughout the medieval period, social and economic change left a powerful imprint on the landscape and, most importantly, what we think of today as characteristic English countryside. For example, great social upheavals such as the fourteenth-century plague have encouraged historians and geographers to identify deserted villages across England. However, in Bedfordshire the traces of these settlements are difficult to spot in the landscape. In some cases the location of a church, now isolated from any habitation, is the best clue.

The best example in Bedfordshire is in the parish of Carlton with Chellington, close to the River Ouse, where the parish church of Saint Nicholas is now at a distance from any habitation. The village was clearly to the east of the church and there are good examples of ridge and furrow plough marks in the fields. Why did the village move? There is no documented evidence, but it may have been the need to be located closer to the bridging point of the Ouse, or a more dramatic event, such as the plague. As in the rest of England, there are numerous references to 'deserted villages' but the cause of desertion is difficult to be precise about.

There seems to have been four main causes. Across England it is estimated that up to one-third of the population perished in the Black Death (1348–50) and in smaller outbreaks later in the fourteenth century. Second, this violent scourge followed a number of poor harvests caused by a worsening climate, and the outbreak of disease therefore cut down a weakened population. Third, there were frequent complaints about the levels of tax being levied. Medieval studies in Bedfordshire based on tax returns have shown that land was being abandoned in the decades before the Black Death.

Historians have suggested that the colder and wetter clay lands, where farmers struggled on the difficult glacial deposits and uplands in north Bedfordshire, were the first to feel the change in climate and economic decline. There are records of parishes such as Keysoe, Bolnhurst and Riseley being unable to meet tax demands. On the Greensand also, marginal land which had been worth clearing in better times was abandoned. At Potton the villagers declared that 'the soil was sandy for the greater part and produced nothing except rye'. Also around Segenhoe (close to modern Ridgmont), some two hundred acres were left un-tilled in 1341.

Finally, as landowners found land to be unprofitable for arable crops, the clearance of land for sheep pastures became popular, and emptied many villages as less labour was required. Most of the deserted settlements were located on the Greensand in Bedfordshire or the northern clay lands, and this distribution is a clue to the falling income from arable agriculture.

The Enclosure Movement

Much of the countryside we see today dates from when the open fields cultivated in strips by medieval farmers were *enclosed*, leaving the unmistakable pattern of ridge and furrow as the only relic of a former agricultural landscape, now swept away. By the end of the seventeenth century an economic revival was underway in the countryside and there was a movement in the Midlands of England to replace tillage by grass, especially on these heavy clay lands where sheep replaced the corn of the medieval peasant. As Hoskins makes clear:

'The eviction of the open field farmers was easy enough. At the end of the farming year immediately after the corn harvest, they were ordered to go; their farmsteads were demolished, and the multitudinous strips of the open fields were laid to grass. The two or three arable fields were replaced by a number of large pastures enclosed by a hawthorn hedge and ditch.'

This phase of enclosure was slow and in 1750 much of Bedfordshire was still a landscape of open fields: a century later almost all the arable strips had been replaced by the formal field pattern of hedged fields common today. This is a landscape of regular-sized fields bounded by hawthorn hedges and ditches, with small nucleated villages linked by broad and often straight enclosure roads. The catalyst for this was the passing of the General Enclosure Act of 1750. Later in the eighteenth century the strain on the English economy of the Napoleonic War, the pressure of additional tax, and the need to feed a growing urban and industrial population, added an immense impetus to enclosure. There was not, however, a national consensus on this far-reaching social movement. On the one hand, the presence of common land was described by one commentator as a 'seminary for a lazy thieving sort of people'. On the other hand, the divorce of the peasantry from the soil and the removal of open field farmers was considered a 'heavy price which the nation ultimately paid for a supply of bread and meat.'

Ridge and furrow remnants in a field at Marston Vale

In this rush to enclose, the influence of the great landlords in spreading improved agricultural techniques was important: the need to improve animal breeding, especially sheep, was a passion of many of these large-scale farmers. Agricultural historians have pointed out that in the period before artificial fertilisers spreading manure was the only way to return fertility to the land.

As livestock numbers were low in the open fields there could never be adequate manure to replace this loss of fertility when crops were harvested. The inherent fertility, and most importantly, the ideal crumb structure of the topsoil, allowing penetration of roots and air into the root zone of plants which had been inherited from the forest, was gradually lost and the open fields were becoming 'dirty' with weeds. Open field agriculture may have already been on the verge of breakdown from advancing soil depletion, and the improving landlords had a sense of this taking place and used this opportunity to reform.

The Act of Enclosure: Setting out the Modern Field Pattern

In the Middle Ages parishes consisted of one or more large common fields divided into open strips un-enclosed by hedges, fences or walls. One person might own a number of strips in a number of fields not in close proximity to one another. Enclosure was a process by which commissioners surveyed the common fields, calculated the size of a person's land holding, assessed the varying quality of the land and then allotted a proportionate amount of land in one or more new, much smaller, fields created out of the common fields and enclosed by a hedge, wall or fence. This gave us our modern landscape of small fields and hedges. This process might be undertaken by private agreement but in Bedfordshire was usually done by Act of Parliament. The enclosure of each parish was carried out by a separate Act. The first Bedfordshire parish to be enclosed by Act of Parliament was Aspley Guise in 1761 and the last was Totternhoe in 1891. Altogether 103 Bedfordshire parishes were enclosed in 95 Acts of Parliament, most in the last quarter of the eighteenth century.

Careful examination of the records and the landscape can distinguish several waves of enclosures. More than half of Bedfordshire had been enclosed in some form or other by the close of the eighteenth century. For example, land around Ampthill was enclosed in 1806 and by this date two-thirds of Bedfordshire was enclosed. The result was smaller fields bounded by newly planted hedges, which are relatively young in ecological terms.

The Influence of the Great and Less Great Parks

Bedfordshire, in common with much of lowland England, owes much to the care, attention, pride and outright rivalry of the landed families, who competed to beautify and develop parks, mostly for their own pleasure. Prior to this movement of competing landowners, the deer parks of England had survived from the Middle Ages: tracts of woodland were protected for hunting, which was followed by not only the kings of England but also a new class of self-made men. Map-makers in the sixteenth and early seventeenth centuries such as Speed and Saxton record these parks and many survive, such as Ampthill Great Park, in the landscape today. The Great Park and Little Park of Ampthill were at their full glory in the time of Henry VIII, and attracted Royal hunting parties in the early sixteenth century. The place name 'Park' on the present-day Ordnance Survey (OS) map is often a sign of the presence of these reserved areas. In some places the old boundary lines of substantial banks and ditches are still evident, such as the boundary lines of Steppingly Deer Park, which is still visible within Flitwick Woods. In time many of these deer parks became the locations of great houses with surrounding gardens and then the park, usually in grassland, was separated from the house by a low wall, ditch or an ingenious landscape device known as a 'ha-ha', which allowed uninterrupted views from the house over the landscaped park without allowing livestock access to the formal gardens. A surviving example of this ingenious landscape feature is still functional today at Flitwick Manor on the outskirts of the town. However, it needs to be remembered that these expensive investments in parks required a shrewd business sense to finance and a return on investment elsewhere in the farming estate.

Woburn Park: a classic example of a parkland landscape

The history of these ventures in land planning and shaping in the county alone would fill a book, and only the most successful of the estates have survived. Others have come and gone: some are now only a name on a map. Each Park has its own unique history shaped by often eccentric landowners, but together they have contributed much to the look and feel of the county. Classic examples are Woburn Park, now an international tourist attraction, adapted to the modern commercial age as a visitor centre.

Wimpole Hall – just across the Cambridgeshire border – is now cared for by the National Trust. The influence of the Park at Wimpole is discernible well beyond the areas close to the 'Big House' and the model home farms clustered around it.

The influence of parks such as Woburn went beyond the planned landscape, and the introduction of exotic animal species such as muntjac deer and the black squirrel to the parks eventually led to escapes and the spread of these animals across lowland England. Muntjac deer, escaping or released from Woburn around 1925, have now spread as far as the Scottish border, possibly aided by more further releases in the north. The spread of black squirrels – a mutation from the common grey – dates from releases from a private collection in Bedfordshire around 1912 and these animals are now found in Hertfordshire, Bedfordshire and into Cambridgeshire.

How old is that Hedge? Hooper's Law has an Answer

During the 1960s the rapid decline in rural wildlife, especially the bird population, was a cause for concern, and researchers tried to unravel the likely factors involved. Pesticides were the initial target but it soon became clear that there existed other influences, including the ploughing of old pasture land, land drainage, or perhaps the removal of hedges. An ecology researcher called Max Hooper looked at the grubbing-up of hedges across southern England using aerial photographic evidence from 1946 onwards and reached the alarming conclusion that during the 1960s some 10,000 miles of hedges were removed. However, he also noted that it was not only the length of hedged land but the quality of mix of trees and woody scrubs in a hedge that was important. Older hedges were more mixed and richer in species, and therefore more valued by wildlife. By sampling over a length of 30 yards using 227 sites in England that could be dated, he reached the conclusion that one species of woody plant for every 100 years was a useful rule of thumb. This is Hooper's law. So, a hedge that could be dated as a Saxon boundary would have some dozen different species in 30 yards and a relatively new enclosure hedge from the mid-nineteenth century would have perhaps two.

Exotic trees from abroad, such as the sycamore, introduced in the sixteenth century to adorn the parks, have become a common species well away from the landed estates; later, cedars and Douglas Fir from abroad were planted.

> ### Contractor and Consultant: Garden Landscape Designers in Bedfordshire
>
> In Bedfordshire the work of two of the greatest eighteenth-century landscape gardeners is still evident at a number of places, as is their contrasting styles. The legacy of Humphry Repton (1752–1818) is perhaps not so well known as that of Lancelot 'Capability' Brown (1716–1783), but his work is impressive. Brown worked at Luton Hoo, Ampthill Park, Southill Park, Woburn Abbey and Wrest Park. At Wrest Park, Brown's enthusiasm for remodelling the landscape was kept in check by Jemima, the Marchioness Grey. Brown was allowed to soften the profile of the gardens and help create the subtle boundary between the formal garden and the agricultural landscape beyond. More typically Brown carved out huge landscapes from older formal gardens and agricultural lands, and is best understood as garden contractor, moulding the landscape to his plans. Repton, in contrast, coined the phrase 'landscape gardener' for himself, and was often called in to refine Brown's work; for example, at Woburn. He also worked at Moggerhanger where his thoughtful design carefully works the house into the overall design, and this approach made him a leader of the 'picturesque movement'. Repton considered himself an improver of landscapes; Brown changed the view. Brown became rich, whereas Repton had a more modest income.

The common Bedfordshire estate cottages in a distinctive red brick are now prized rural housing and add a familiar architectural note to anyone travelling through the county. As the fashion for parks spread outwards to the minor gentry, competition between surveyors and landscape engineers to map and improve the estates intensified. The major stars in this movement were undoubtedly talented men such as 'England's Great Gardener', 'Capability' Brown, who counted the most wealthy as patrons in the middle of the eighteenth century.

Forestry in the Landscape

A view of rural Bedfordshire from the air on a flight into Luton Airport is a reminder of how much woodland survives or has been planted in the county. However, Bedfordshire remains one of the least wooded counties in England and in Britain overall the proportion of woodland remains low compared to Europe. England has less than a 10 per cent cover of woodland compared to France with 25 per cent, Germany with 20 per cent and Spain with 24 per cent cover. The pulse of woodland clearance and planting has been present since the first clearances, dictated by economic factors and political considerations. Understanding these changes provides an insight into the woodland pattern across the present landscape.

It is well documented that the reduction in woodland across England continued as population and farming expanded. Farmers cleared natural forest where the soils were amenable to farming and in areas where soils were wet and cold woodland survived longest. Records from the Domesday Book in the county note the importance of woodland for the fattening of pigs on 'mast',[2] or food for swine. Land at Meppershall was given additional value in the Domesday record as it provided feeding for 200 swine, and at Haynes 500 pigs were recorded. Woodland was also used for hunting, and this ensured its survival until rural economies began to seek out good timber for domestic buildings and later for shipbuilding.

The importance of managed woodland in the economy of the medieval landowner is demonstrated by the substantial boundary ditch and bank along the edge of Kings Wood, close to Rushmere Country Park. This ditch, which is estimated to date from the thirteenth century, separates the valuable wood managed by coppicing from the adjacent Rammamere Common which, as the name suggests, was open to use by all. The remaining woodland at Kings Wood is now one of the few National Nature Reserves (NNRs) located in Bedfordshire.

By the seventeenth century timber was becoming scarce. Across Bedfordshire small brickworks were springing up and timber houses and farm buildings were being replaced by stone or brick. Woodland did survive in patches, such as in the Kings Wood on the boulder clay east of Ampthill, in Odell Great Wood, and most interestingly in Marston Thrift, now a part of the new Marston Vale Forest Park. The influence of soils and topography was critical here. The greatest concentration of older woodland was allowed to remain on the Greensand Ridge and adjacent areas where there were well established and managed large estates, which valued woodland as a part of the estate income, not only from the timber but also as a source of revenue from regular shoots. In this regard the Woburn Estate is interesting, as detailed records were kept.

The acceleration of woodland clearance in the sixteenth and seventeenth centuries must have resulted in Bedfordshire being as open and as devoid of woodland as at any time in its history. The large expanses of open fields

(2) Mast' is the edible seeds and fruits in autumn, usually acorns: 2013 was a very prolific mast year.

uninterrupted by the hedges we recognise today would have looked somewhat like the landscape we now associate with neighbouring counties to the east, such as Cambridgeshire. The Parliamentary enclosures then broke up these arable plains into hedged fields with ditches planted with fast-growing thorn and spaced with elms, which we would recognise and perhaps assume as the natural landscape pattern in Bedfordshire. Thus, we arrive at the basic framework of the countryside today.

As noted elsewhere, the influence of the large estates in the past has been critical in managing the landscape for both economic return and pleasure. There has been a tradition of tree planting on the Duke of Bedford Estate, for example, and at the beginning of the twentieth century the estate embarked on several extensive planting schemes. By the outbreak of the Second World War the estate is reported to have planted some six million trees, which became an important source of pit props during the war for the Midland collieries.

The realisation that timber was a critical resource was brought home in 1945 and led to the foundation of the Forestry Commission nationally, and extensive plantings of imported soft woods. This public planting was also augmented by the incentives offered on forestry planting by tax inducements in the 1970s: new forests were created or older areas expanded or came within Forestry Commission management. Maulden Forest became a feature of the landscape in Bedfordshire and is interesting, as the new planting is mostly on the more difficult sandy soils and broken topography of the Greenland Ridge. Part of the woodland was eventually designated as a Site of Special Scientific Interest (SSSI) for the acidic grassland and heathland interest: wildlife includes badgers, foxes and barn owls, and overall the site is important for invertebrates and plants which respond to the variation in soil type, from clay to sandy gravel.

The northern end of the wood is also an SSSI because of its importance as one of Bedfordshire's largest remnants of ancient woodland, in addition to the nearby Kings Wood. The southern end of the wood is sometimes called Pennyfather's Wood and is situated on Greensand, whereas the rest of Maulden Wood is situated on a cap of glacial boulder clay. This landscape, with sudden steep dry valleys and views across the valley of the Flit, has become a valued recreation area for walkers and a feature of the long-distance Greensand Ridge Path. In 2011 the government announced plans for a national sale of forested land managed by the Forestry Commission, which raised the possibility of limited public access for future generations, but this measure was defeated in the face of national opposition.

Bedfordshire is fortunate to have a number of relic woodland sites remaining simply because they were not attractive to cultivation in the past. The Ancient Woodland Project is now taking an interest in the management of these sites and a number of 'clusters', where there are scattered woods that are relics of ancient woodland, are now being targeted for sensitive management. One such cluster is in the east of the county in the Potton–Cockyane Hatley area. These sites are, of course, now important both scientifically and as recreation areas.

Another example is Southill SSSI, which incorporates a wet area caused by a spring at the junction of the permeable greensand and the less permeable Gault Clay; Cooper's Hill SSSI on the outskirts of Ampthill, which was shunned by farmers due to the steep slopes and sandy soils of the Greensand; and the 'hangers or clangers' (as they are known in Bedfordshire) of ancient woodland remaining in the steep valleys on the edge of the chalk.

Finally, as the environmental movement caught the attention of planners and the public, a conscious move to increase woodland and plant trees where possible has taken root. In Bedfordshire this has led to the planting of fast-growing species, such as poplars, by private landowners. In the more extensive plantings associated with the Millennium Forest project in Marston Vale, the approach has been to plant mixed woodland, using saplings grown from seed harvested locally, if at all possible. In addition to the new planting, the Marston Vale initiative has attempted to conserve and bring under progressive management older woodland, encouraging all the residents of the county to take an interest in the ambitious venture of creating a new forest, which is mixed in age as well as in species.

Despite these recent initiatives, woodland cover for Bedfordshire is still below the national average, and in an effort to encourage landowners to invest in trees, a number of Farm Woodland Demonstration Sites have been launched. With support from the European Commission and local government, some 50 hectares of small woods have been planted, including a demonstration site at Clapham Park, north of Bedford.

The Modern Landscape

Bedfordshire is still a farming county and agriculture a major industry. However, the influence of farming on the countryside is no longer the only, or even perhaps the dominant, force, and farmers are mindful of the funds available for good stewardship of the landscape. There are now arrays of schemes to encourage partnerships with conservation organisations, and this has slowed the removal of hedgerows which was once so common. Wider 'headlands' along the edge of fields are welcomed by walkers and are important for ground-nesting birds, and it is now common to see corners of fields planted with trees. The largest influence has been the change in public attitude to the countryside, which has encouraged multiple uses. Landowners, if commercially minded, can profit from visitors or regular users of the world outdoors.

The management of land for lowland shoots has, for example, done much to retain cover in the form of small copses and hedgerows. Many of the larger farms have profited from farm conversions of outbuildings to become rural offices and workshops. Most villages in the county now have nearby a number of electrically fenced paddocks catering for the growth of equestrian sports; the Forestry Commission and private woodland owners have opened up sites for cross-county cycling – it is difficult in Bedfordshire to justify the term 'mountain biking'; and there is now a dedicated partnership between local government and the Ramblers (formerly known as the Ramblers' Association) to ensure that the footpaths network is maintained and kept open.

Recreational use also extends to the reclamation of land damaged by past use by the mineral extraction industry, the most obvious example being the Marston Vale Forest and the use of the gravel pits by water sports enthusiasts. Conservation organisations are prominent in the management of the countryside and volunteers are welcome to help the Wildlife Trusts and the Greensand Trust. All of this interest and work is beginning to make an impact on what we see in the Bedfordshire landscape.

There is legitimate concern when these developments reach large-scale commercial importance, such as the new Center Parcs development in the plantations of the Greensand Ridge. Historically, this is another example of difficult land for farming being put to an alternative use.

The mineral extraction industry within the county has always been important and has resulted in abandoned workings in all the landscape types, including the chalk pits in the south of the county, the now water-filled brick pits on Oxford Clay, the gravel extraction workings in the Ouse and Ivel Valleys, and sand extraction from the Greensand, especially around Leighton Buzzard. Rather than these legacies of a past industrial age being seen as a problem, they have become an opportunity. The splendid marina and Priory Country Park in Bedford is an outstanding example providing open space for the large urban population of Bedford, and there is a plan to extend this recreational zone eastwards to become the Bedford River Valley Park, stretching along the Ouse Valley.

Small Scale Wine Production at Warden Vinyard

More extensive development will be inevitable in the next decade, as the county struggles to find the space to meet national government expectations that Bedfordshire will contribute to new housing for the south-east of England. In the past, new town developments for the south-east have been in surrounding counties, such as at Milton Keynes, in Buckinghamshire, and in Bedfordshire development has been on the fringes of the main centres of Bedford and Luton and in-filling in the villages. Flat land is at a premium for building, making sites such as the Ouse floodplain and the Wixams development (tacked on to the very edge of Bedford), very valuable for house building.

The Wixams development is on the difficult-to-drain clays of the Marston Vale; the Ouse Valley is development on the low terrace gravels adjacent to the floodplain. While these terraces are amenable to building, future river levels and the frequency of major flood events are difficult to predict. Greater run-off as more land is paved, less predictable climatic patterns, a lack of funds for river maintenance, the balance between conservation demands and river flows and the rising cost of insurance cover all combine to warn against building on floodplains.

With this increased pressure on space in such a small county as Bedfordshire, the importance of the planners working with the growing conservation movement is critical, as is the framework for public consultation. The growth of interest in outdoor leisure pursuits will inevitably bring some conflict. The use of bridleways, footpaths and cycleways will need a degree of tolerance from each user group, for example.

However, what is encouraging is the mushrooming of public interest and the creative use of land often thought to be blighted by a former use to create a sprinkling of nature and protected reserves across the county. Returning former sand pits – such as the Sandhouse Pit at Heath and Reach – to use as nature reserves, with the active involvement of the extraction company, is an encouraging example. This site and others in Bedfordshire underline the work of the Greensand Trust, and pressure groups such as ramblers' organisations all provide a channel for the interested public to understand and contribute more.

This account of the landscape in Bedfordshire will hopefully help readers to understand why the countryside looks as it does today; why change is not necessarily a bad thing; and why an informed public is the best defence against lax planning. A graphic pictorial example of the change from the early eighteenth century is now readily accessible through the innovative publication of older editions of OS maps (see Further Reading for details).

Britain's Nineteenth-century Landscape in Maps

Maps based on Britain's first national mapping project, the Ordnance Survey's One-Inch ('Old Series'), which were first published between 1805 and 1874, are now available in a format which has been re-projected and enlarged to match the present-day Ordnance Survey. Therefore each of these maps (published by Cassini) is directly comparable with the corresponding Ordnance Survey contemporary 1:50,000 scale Landranger series, and uses the same sheet number and grid references, enabling the past and the present to be compared with ease and accuracy. All the Old Series maps of England and Wales (123 in total) have now been published. A good example is Old Series 153 – Bedford and Huntingdon sheet. Also available are all the Old Series maps in a boxed set for the present OS Sheet 153, and these are from three different periods, designed to appeal to anyone who wants to discover the hidden history of their local landscape. This set includes the Old Series described above, Revised New Series Maps first published between 1896 and 1904, and the Popular Edition Maps first published between 1919 and 1926.

Ramblers use a footpath across arable land in north Bedfordshire

CHAPTER 2

SCARPS AND VALES

There is now increasing attention being given to conserving and maintaining what we refer to as the English countryside, but understanding what exactly gives each locality its own character and sense of place, and what makes it different from neighbouring areas, is often not immediately obvious. This chapter suggests that the underlying geology is the dominant influence when attempting to define landscape character.

The Chilterns: a dry valley in chalk above Barton. A landscape of 'distinctive character' as defined by the Countryside Agency

Bedfordshire has been described as a county of scarps and vales, hence the title of this chapter. To unravel the clues which help us understand the present-day landscape, this book has been laid out in sections, each of which describes the landscape typical of a specific area, beginning with the geology and followed by some observations on the soils, the resulting land use and agriculture. Then I have added a few notes on the way in which the land was used in the past and what contributes to the appearance of the landscape as we view it today. Using this framework, it is possible to divide Bedfordshire into five broad areas, based on geology. In most cases it is also possible to subdivide these further into more specific areas of landscape which are easily recognised, each having distinctive characteristics.

A Portrait of Bedfordshire by David Kennett (1978) used the geology to subdivide the county. Chapters in his book are entitled 'The Stone Country', where the River Ouse has eroded into the distinctive cream–brown limestone known as oolite; 'The Chalk County', around Luton; and 'The Brick Country' in mid Bedfordshire.

The concern to conserve buildings and landscapes has prompted planners to try to define what exactly gives an area local and specific character: this is often an elusive idea. For example, the Countryside Agency has undertaken a Landscape Character Assessment throughout both England and Scotland (this ambitious scheme was first published in 2002 and a review was announced in 2010), and in Bedfordshire there are four such areas listed: the Chilterns, the Bedfordshire Greensand Ridge, the Bedfordshire Clay Plain and the East Anglia Chalk. Descriptions of each give systematic information on the features and characteristics that add a distinctive look and feel to each locality. Such a framework was envisaged as being useful to planners, conservation groups and those engaged in environmental improvement schemes for areas undergoing regeneration. This system is now administered by Natural England and in some counties in England has been overlain by a Historic Landscape Assessment, which integrates the perceived landscape value with historical information, such as archaeological sites.

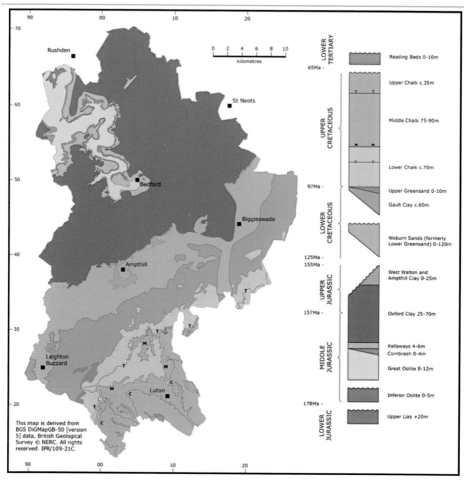

Map 2.1. The solid geology of Bedfordshire (1984 Bedfordshire County Council).

The framework used in this book builds on this broad-brush classification of landscape and fills in more detail, making the scale more relevant to the casual observer. Most importantly, the chapters that follow explain more of the history which lies behind the present-day appearance of the countryside, and also expands on the previous and current use of the land. Map 2.1 illustrates the distribution of the solid geology in Bedfordshire and this is followed by Table 2.1, which sets out the sequence of rock formations in the county. These provide basic building blocks which are used throughout the book: each section then provides an overview of a characteristic landscape. The distribution of these landscapes is illustrated in Map 2.2, and each is described in Table 2.2.

Table 2.1 Geology of Bedfordshire

Geological period	Bedfordshire formation	Description of rocks	Location in Beds
RECENT	Alluvium	Sediments since the end of the last glaciation	More recent valley deposits; peat in the Flit valley
PLEISTOCENE	Glacial Deposits	Some of the river gravels; boulder clays from the last glacial period; brickearths from earlier cold dry periods	North and mid Bedfordshire glacial clays forming the low hills around Pulloxhill and on the Greensands Ridge; also north of Bedford. Brickearth deposit south of Luton
PALAEOCENE	Reading Beds	A non-marine deposit of red and mottled clays below the London Clays	Kensworth quarry
		Beginning of Alpine and Miocene Folding which created the Chilterns	
CRETACEOUS	Upper Chalk	Denudation has removed much of the upper levels of chalk	Skimpot quarry
	Middle Chalk	Cream chalk, sometimes white with flints, includes the *Melbourne Beds*, a hard yellowish chalk with nodules	At the foot of the Downs - Houghton Regis, for example
	Lower Chalk	Chalky clay - soft pale grey or cream. Chalk marl (includes *Totternhoe Stone*).	

Geological period	Bedfordshire formation	Description of rocks	Location in Beds
	Gault Clay	Stiff clay, tenacious and dark in colour	Narrow strip across the county - exposed in former brick workings at Harlington
	Lower Greensand	Marine deposits in shifting sandbanks with rapid currents. Porous water bearing. Variety of sand types	Leighton Buzzard sand pits, Ampthill Park, Sandy, Warren, Fuller's Earth pits at Clophill
JURASSIC			
	Ampthill Clay	Dark or black clay	Few exposure - records only from the Ampthill railway tunnel
	Oxford clay	Stiff and tenacious. Bluish-grey in colour; reptile and ammonite fossils	Some 500 feet thick. Exposed in the Marston Vale brick pits
	Cornbrash	So named because they provide a stony or 'brashy' soil favourable to growing corn. Rubbly bed of limestone laid in shallow water.	Thin band only along the Ouse close to Bletsoe, north of Sharnbrook and Souldrop
	Blisworth Clay	Clay band containing oyster shells	
	Great Oolite	Limestone well bedded and separated by clay or marl bands	Turvey and Stevington, Classic building stone or north Beds

Scarps and Vales

The Geology of Buildings: Looking at the Stonework

An understanding of the regional geology is often best demonstrated by the choice of building materials, especially stonework. As a general rule, the older a building, the more likely it is to be constructed from local materials. The cost of transport was a large part of the overall cost of construction, especially before rail and canal routes reduced costs. In Bedfordshire older buildings, especially medieval churches, therefore directly reflect the availability of local building stone or brick-making clays. These buildings are strong clues to the local geology, and a selection of representative examples are given below.

Someries Castle, a mid-fifteenth-century construction situated close to Luton Airport, is the earliest brick-built building in the county, with fine examples of decorative **brickwork**. Local clays from the drifts overlying the chalk were the source of these bricks. **Houghton House** outside Ampthill is a later seventeenth-century brick building.

Bromham Bridge and older houses in **Harrold,** and other north Bedfordshire villages, are constructed from **Great Oolitic limestone** quarried from a thin strip of land on the valley sides of the River Ouse in the vicinity of Bromham, Oakley, Pavenham and Milton Ernest.

The traditional **almshouses** in **Leighton Buzzard, and old St Mary's Church, Clophill**, are good examples of the use of the **Lower Greensand**. This is a friable building stone, reddish-brown in colour.

Husborne Crawley Church uses both stone from the Upper Greensand (which contains the distinctive green mineral, glauconite, from which these sandstone rocks take their name) and the less resistant Lower Greensand. The **Upper Greensand** is a very durable stone, but outcrops are less common. The green colouration in the facing stones makes this church worth a visit.

Woburn Abbey is the best-known local building constructed from local **Totternhoe Stone**, which is quarried along the northern slope of the Lower Chalk. This is a very versatile rock, which was laid down in thin beds during pauses in sedimentation. Quarries along the slope between Totternhoe and Sewell have extensive workings, some underground, dating from the eighteenth century.

Houghton Regis and **Barton Churches** are only two of the many local medieval buildings which are decorated in elaborate chequerboard patterns of alternating **chalk and flint**. Flint is a pure silica and very durable, lasting longer than the matrix in which it is set. One attraction of flint is that stones can be easily collected from the chalk.

Table 2.2: Landscapes of Bedfordshire

Code	Area	Landscape type	Characteristic area
1	*The Chalk Downs and Plateau of south Bedfordshire*		
1a		The chalk scarp and Downs	Dunstable Downs and areas such as Clappers
1b		The 'clay with flints' plateau	South of Luton, around Caddington and into Hertfordshire
1c		The Icknield Loam Belt	Eddlesborough, Houghton Regis
2	*The Clay Vales of mid Bedfordshire*		
2a		The Gault Clay lowlands	Tilsworth, Gravenhurts to Wimpole Hall in the east
2b		The Oxford Clays	Marston Vale
3	*The Greensand Ridge*		
		The Greensand Ridge	Aspley Heath, Woburn, Ampthill Park, Sandy Warren
4	*The Boulder Clay Uplands*		
4a		Mid Bedfordshire Hills	From Cranfield in the west, Pulloxhill, Haynes and east of Biggleswade
4b		North Bedfordshire Uplands	Renhold and north to border with Northamptonshire and south to Cranfield
5	*The Ouse and Ivel Valleys*		
5a		Ouse Valley	Cardington, Bromham, Oakley on the Ouse
5b		Ivel Valley	Along the Ivel Valley to Langford
5c		Flit Vale	Flitwick Moor
5d		Lea Valley	South of Luton
5e		Kym Valleys	Draining towards Kimbolton

Map 2.2: Landscapes of Bedfordshire

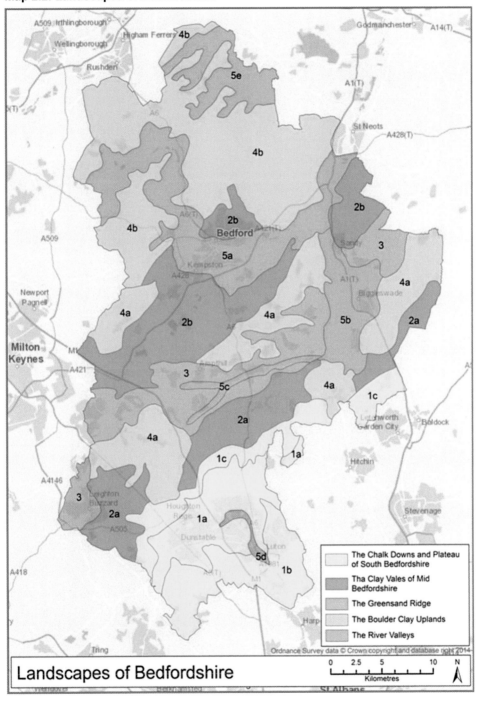

The Chalk Downs and Plateau of South Bedfordshire

Tha Clay Vales of Mid Bedfordshire

The Greensand Ridge

The Boulder Clay Uplands

The River Valleys

Ordnance Survey data © Crown copyright and database right 2014

Landscapes of Bedfordshire

0   2.5   5   10   N
Kilometres

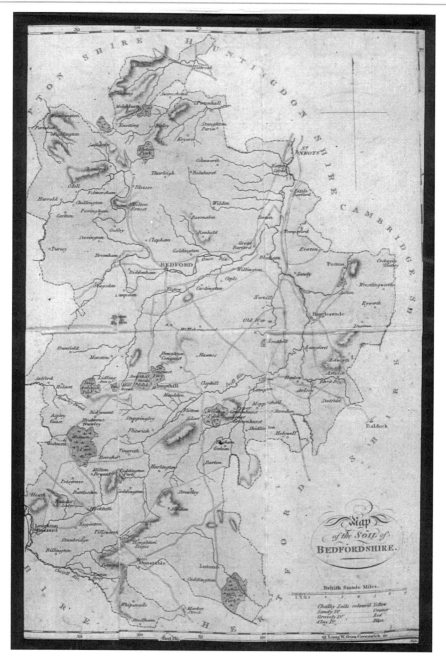

Map by Thomas Batchelor ~
Soil of Bedfordshire, dated 1813

Scarps and Vales

Not Just a Hole in the Ground: Mineral Resources in Bedfordshire

The extraction industries have always been a major economic activity in Bedfordshire. In 1972 a county-wide review by the County Council Planning Department listed 216 pits, both active and abandoned. In the mid-1990s, the British Geological Survey and the Department of the Environment produced a county map which recorded the broad distribution of economic mineral resources for Bedfordshire. As these maps also noted the distribution of conservation areas such as Sites of Special Scientific Interest (SSSIs) and scheduled and ancient monuments, the idea was that the map provided an easy pictorial reference for planners. As these sites have a striking impact on landscape, the character and main features of each group are noted below.

The Chalk. *This extensive outcrop in the southern part of the county is quarried for chalk marl towards the base of the formation, at the Houghton Regis and Sundon sites. This marl is characterised by a high clay content which is ideal for cement manufacture. Also from the Lower Chalk, Totternhoe Stone is extracted on a small scale as a building stone now used for restoration work: repairs carried out on the parish church at Barton are an example. The Middle Chalk, in contrast, has a higher purity, and the quarries at Kensworth are an example.*

The Greensand. *In the past there were many local quarries for building stone extracted from the Greensand, and numerous local churches and other older buildings are constructed from this rather flaky erodible material. Better known are the numerous bedrock sand quarries from the Woburn Sands Formation within the Greensand belt. Extraction centres on Leighton Buzzard and Potton. In the Heath and Reach area, pure silica sand is extracted; otherwise, the main use is for building sand. Finally, there is a long history of Fuller's Earth extraction in Bedfordshire, and the county provides rare exposures of this clay, which has a wide range of industrial applications and is in demand for drilling mud in the North Sea oil and gas industry. The main site now is at Woburn Sands.*

The Brick Clays. *The Lower Oxford Clay of Marston Vale was at one time one of the major sources of brick clay in the UK. The high carbon content, at around 5 per cent, acts as an internal fuel during firing and reduces fuel costs. The dimensions of the clay pits, such as Quest, are due to unsuitable Middle and Upper Oxford Clay which needs to be removed as an overburden. In the past the Gault Clay was also used, but was more difficult to utilise economically: the pits at Arlesey are a relic of this operation.*

The Brick Earths. *These are scattered and now largely unworked deposits, which at one time provided a source of brick-making material, especially in the south of the county. Brick earths were formed from windblown fine silt or clays which was usually deposited in landscape hollows during glacial periods There was a site at Caddington, south of Luton, which produced a distinctive bluish brick.*

Sand and Gravel. *These are mostly river terrace deposits along the Ouse and Ivel, which are now popular for house building development. Ongoing extraction operations are at Broom and at Willington; relic pits are common along the Ouse and Ivel valleys.*

Sand and gravel extraction near Broom from the Ivel River

CHAPTER 3

THE CHALK LANDS

The chalk hills in south Bedfordshire are perhaps the most dramatic landscapes within the county. Gliders from the Dunstable Downs launch site and kite fliers make use of the updrafts created by the favourable topography, illustrating how important this landscape is to the public. The white chalk exposure outlining a lion below the zoo site at Whipsnade makes the geological skeleton of the county very clear. The scarps which face north and west provide panoramic views of the clay vales and onwards to the Greensand Ridge in the distance. Looking south and east, the cereal fields and woodlands blend into Hertfordshire. However, even within this familiar landscape there are subtle variations. This chapter explains how these variations influence the way in which the chalk countryside is used and appears today.

The Icknield Way close to Dunstable

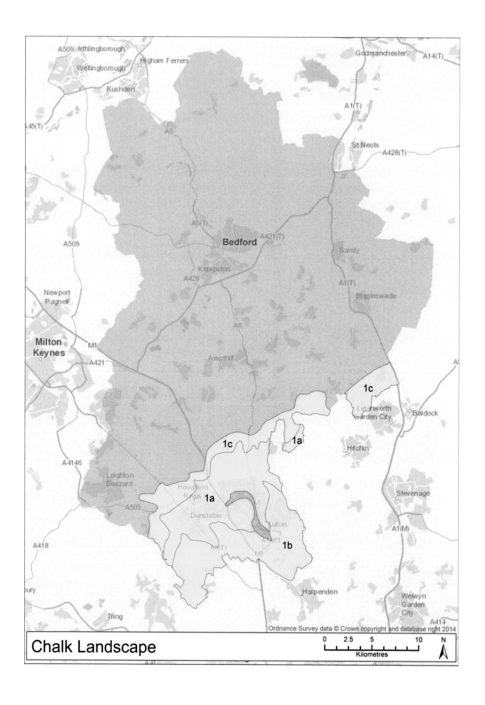

Chalk Landscape

The Chalk Scarps

In southern England the chalk uplands are perhaps the most distinctive of all landscapes and this is also true in Bedfordshire. Anyone familiar with the South or North Downs will recognise the chalk landscape, with its wide expanses of short-cropped turf often grazed by sheep, fronted by steep slopes offering expansive views across the clay vale below, and beyond to the Greensand Ridge. The north- and west-facing scarp slope is backed by the gentle dip slope running south and east into the gentle saucer-like topography of the London Basin. The eastern Chilterns, which stretch into Bedfordshire in the south of the county, provide a great vantage point and the resistant Upper and Middle Cretaceous chalk rock formations define the character of southern Bedfordshire. The striking views from the Dunstable Downs are perhaps the best example of this landscape, and also well known to the residents of Luton are the public areas at Sharpenhoe, Sundon and the Barton Hills. These chalk uplands are aligned north-east to south-west across the county from Baldock to Totternhoe. However, eastwards the hill front is less prominent and the boundary with the clay lowlands is gradual and less distinct.

The Icknield Way is an ancient route which hugs the dry upland scarp edge, avoiding the clay lands to the north and west: Neolithic peoples, the Romans, Saxons, Vikings, Christian pilgrims and today's long-distance walkers have all utilised this route, which takes its name from the Iceni tribe – an Iron Age tribal grouping led at one point by Boudicca in a revolt against the Romans in Britain. In places the Icknield Way is a series of roughly parallel tracks cut through ancient woodland by herdsmen. The linking together of these ancient tracks across the chalk of the English lowlands has resulted in a 170-mile long-distance route for walkers, off-road cyclists and horse riders from the Norfolk coast to Dorset. This route is seldom a single path, and one writer described it as 'a skein of parallel tracks' – sometimes spread over a mile of chalk.

The importance of this east–west route throughout history is marked by the abundance of archaeological features along its length. In Bedfordshire the Five Knolls Bronze Age cairns close to the edge of the scarp north of Dunstable are typical of the many features along this ancient travellers' way. Ravensburgh Castle is the best preserved of the remaining Iron Age forts, and sits in a commanding position above Hexton, but its striking position has suffered from being obscured by thick tree growth. The Icknield Way has now become a challenge for ramblers rather than pilgrims, and this is described further in Chapter 10. This pathway follows the edge of the steep scarp slope which is such a striking feature that it is visible viewed from the north. The poet Edward Thomas walked this route in 1911 and produced an unconventional guide, which mixes history, geology and poetry. As he was in the grip of poetical depression at the time, his guide is interesting but not the best companion for a relaxing stroll.

The geology of the chalk in Bedfordshire is more complex than first appears, with outcrops of Lower, Middle and Upper Chalk all contributing to the landscape pattern. The Upper Chalk is best viewed as the feature which forms the main and impressive escarpments around Luton. The rock itself is actually a particularly pure white limestone, built from the microscopic organism *foraminifera*, together with larger shells and fine-grained calcium carbonate. The lower parts of the formation are more clay-rich.

Although the chalk appears to be a uniform geology and the outcrops in Bedfordshire are characterised by almost horizontal strata, some of these layers are much harder and more resistant than others, and add to the landscape detail, especially in the west of the county. The chalk at Totternhoe gives its name to the Totternhoe Rock which is representative of the Lower Chalk. These beds are rich in stones and nodules in a chalk matrix and were once a valued building stone, quarried historically by the monks of Dunstable Priory. There is still a specialist demand for restoration work.

A ubiquitous component of all the chalk strata is the presence of flint – which is likely to occur as isolated nodules some 10 centimetres or more across. These flints are black or brown and the outside white, where they merge into the chalk rock. Flint is a form of silica which is both hard and insoluble; therefore any disintegration or solution of the chalk will leave a flint nodule behind. These nodules are very resistant and form the flint gravels of the alluvium and the main component of the superficial materials and soils on the chalk plateau. The silica is likely to be derived from the skeletons of the sponges which lived in the seas when the chalk was being deposited. Geologists are sure that flints are concretions, and that they are of secondary origin, formed after the rocks were elevated above sea level. This allowed the silica to be concentrated along the layers following the beds of the chalk. The Cretaceous rocks are often visible through the thin soil and grass cover, and the white gash of the chalk quarries is common in this landscape. Beech is a familiar tree on steeper and more protected slopes, otherwise the land use of these scarp slopes is used for sheep grazing and much is now given over to recreational land. Villages such as Edlesborough tend to cling to the foot of the escarpment, where spring lines emerge, at the junction of the permeable chalk rock and the less permeable clay. Slopes are steep – usually too steep for arable agriculture – and woodland has clung to these steeper valleys, which are known as 'hangers'. Just like everywhere else in England, it is impossible to escape the influence of the glaciations. One of the many ice advances during this long cold period, now called the Anglian Glaciation by geologists, reached at least to the foot of the scarp slopes along the north-facing Chiltern Hills.

One probable relic feature of this ice advance is the chalk dry valleys such as at Barton, Pegston and Ravensburgh. These form very steep-sided incisions into the escarpment face and one explanation for them is the action of meltwater from the nearby ice sheets which may have stood against this prominent scarp landscape feature during a penultimate phase of glaciation. These steep slopes and nearness of chalk to the surface are the dominant feature of the soils which are technically described as 'rendzina' by the Soil Survey of England & Wales, in the national mapping of 1984. In general, the soils are thin over the chalk bedrock, with abundant flints.

Chalk Grassland: Sheep-walks and their Legacy

The chalk country of the Eastern Chilterns was land once covered by forest, which was then cleared by the early settlers, using simple tools. This land was easier to clear than the heavy clay vales, and the signs of arable land use are still evident in the lynchets on the chalk slopes. Ultimately this cultivation was replaced by grazing animals, especially sheep, and the traditional chalk grassland or 'sheepwalks' resulted, reaching their greatest extent in the Middle Ages. The chalk grasslands we can enjoy today are therefore a creation of the grazing habit of sheep which allowed a specialist and adapted community of plants to become dominant. Both plants and insects, especially butterflies, filled this ecological niche and after the sheep grazing declined, rabbits took over to retain this short turf grassland. The main point is that this vegetation type is entirely dependent on grazing for its continued existence, without which shrub vegetation encroaches rapidly. This lesson is not lost on modern conservation managers, who work with graziers to maintain this ecological balance. These chalk grasslands areas are highly valued, as the high density of often colourful flowering plants makes these attractive and contrasts with the uniform green of improved grassland, or the arable land nearby. In Bedfordshire the Dunstable Downs provide the most accessible example of this unique habitat.

Dry Valleys in the Chalk: Where has all the Water Gone?

Chalk rocks are permeable and therefore overland flows of water sufficient to carve out a steep-sided valley, such as those which form attractive landscape features along the Chilterns scarp, are difficult to explain. The Windy Hollow dry valley above Barton is a good example, cut into the steep scarp face of the chalk. There are several theories as to how these valleys were cut, the most persuasive of which is that during the ice age the Chilterns area experienced tundra-like conditions, with the subsoil frozen. The normally permeable chalk would have been made impervious by frozen water held within pores in the subsoil and rock. This created 'permafrost', which is common in the Arctic today. Thus water flowed overland, creating streams that carved a valley as water normally does. When the climate warmed, the frozen water in the chalk rock and held in the subsoil pores began to thaw, and water again permeated into the rock, as it does today. There are rare observations of similar conditions historically. In January 1887, the Chalk Wolds of East Yorkshire suffered a succession of frosts which made the ground so hard that no rain could penetrate, and what little rain fell was quickly converted into ice. The same thing happened with regard to subsequent light falls of snow, which partially melted and froze again. On a sudden thaw over a few hours the valley bottoms were converted into torrents, as the ground was still frozen hard underneath. The melting snow could not penetrate, and so 'rivers ran in dry places'. In some villages, which lay in hollows, considerable damage was done to buildings.

The wide open expanses of the Dunstable Downs, previously extensive sheep pasture, is now an important recreation resource for the crowded population of south Bedfordshire. This is typical of the way in which land use has altered in response to pressure on space and the limited ways in which these steep slopes can be used agriculturally. The natural habitat for this landscape would have been a herb-rich grassland, but this is now rare. One species, the very rare Man Orchid (*Orchis anthropophora)*, is only found in Bedfordshire. The botany of these short grasslands has long been recognised as important for butterflies and wild flowers. Sheep grazing is an integral part of the management of this landscape, without which shrub encroachment is very rapid, and this is now being encouraged by conservation agencies engaged in land management. Experiments in natural grazing management have been carried out in a Site of Special Scientific Interest (SSSI), which is within the grounds of Whipsnade Zoo.

Here a rare breed of badger-faced sheep are used and there is, at times, controlled grazing by the zoo elephants.

Barn Hole at Pegsdon: A dry valley in the chalk

There are still relics of beech forest in some of the steeper slopes, but the beech woods are more common on the clays which characterise the plateau and further west in the Chilterns. There is ample evidence from archaeology and the historical record of how important this landscape was. The thin soils on these scarps were easily cleared, which enabled the Icknield Way to provide a historic east–west transit across lowland England. The steep slopes rule out mechanised arable agriculture today, but there is some evidence of past cultivation: the presence of strip lynchets (or terraces) above Barton is a relic of this former cultivation, probably by hand. However, sustained cultivation was never possible and chalk grassland, often with attractive wild flowers, replaced crops. Another former use was the rearing of rabbits in warrens, which are favoured in these well-drained soils. More recently, heavy use of the footpaths by walkers or bridleways used by horses has caused erosion, producing ugly scars on the hillsides.

A typical Rendzina thin soil on the chalk scarp
(Photo from the Soil Survey of England & Wales. Collection held by Cranfield University)

The newly opened visitor centre and extensive car parks now on Dunstable Downs focus on a café and unfortunately lose the opportunity to provide a window of interpretation onto this unique landscape, which is also designated as an SSSI. However, there are many pleasant walks from the centre that link to the long-distance path of the Icknield Way, providing excellent views north and west into the Vale of Aylesbury and the Gault Clays around Barton. By planning a walk from the visitor centre it is also possible to experience the less dramatic landscape on the dip slope, with walks through beech woods and across arable land, which tends to be wet in winter and bone-dry in summer. Further east beyond the A1, the Icknield Way gives access to wonderful country; around Ashwell, for example. Other areas where it is possible to walk in open country are Dunstable Downs, Sundon Hills, Sharpenhoe Clappers and the Barton Hills.

The importance of Dunstable as a settlement on the pilgrim route is marked by the Priory, which dates from the twelfth century. The growth of this monastic site impacted on much of the rural Bedfordshire economy, and its demise in the sixteenth century also can be traced in the agricultural history.

Dunstable Priory: A Medieval Agri-Business

The rural economy of England prior to the Reformation was greatly influenced by the Church and all its institutions, through the ownership of land and the collection of taxes and tithes. By the time of the Dissolution of the Monasteries in the mid-sixteenth century, it was estimated that some 40 per cent of the economy of the state was in the hands of the Church. In Bedfordshire the Augustine Priory, funded by Henry I in 1132 at the meeting place of Watling Street and the Icknield Way, was built by clearing forest, which provided an initial income from timber, later to be augmented by a quarry at Totternhoe, and huge flocks of sheep on the Downs. Tithes were paid by numerous parish churches in Bedfordshire and beyond, and there was a tax on pilgrims. The Priory grew to become a thriving business. When Henry VIII initiated the move to close these institutions, monastic life at Dunstable came to an end in early 1540. Some £350 was raised from the sale, a value in present terms well beyond one million pounds. More importantly, this shift in the economy of rural England led to a property boom and an injection of cash, much of which was invested in agricultural improvement.

The Clay with Flints Plateau

If the steep north- and west-facing chalk scarp slope is the distinctive element of the Bedfordshire landscape, then the matching 'dip slope', stretching south and west away from this edge to the Vale of St Albans, is the more extensive. This 'dip slope' is often described by geologists as the 'clay with flints' plateau. Characterised by large arable fields interspersed with woods (often beech), the clay soils will be recognised by any walker who has ever tramped with mud-clogged boots, swollen to twice the normal size by a mass of sticky grey clay, impossible to shake off. This gentle dip slope is broken by the winding valleys of southward-draining steams such as the Lee.

The solid geology of this plateau is the Middle and Lower Chalk, but the important characteristic of this landscape is the superficial covering of sticky clay with flint stones. Often referred to as either 'clay with flints' or 'plateau drift', this blankets a gently sloping well-wooded landscape where arable agriculture is dominant. The exact origin of these deposits is at the centre of a debate, and there are many academic papers that try to unravel the processes and chronology of these 'drifts' or superficial deposits which lie on top of the solid chalk. It is generally accepted that the presence of ice against the chalk scarp to the north during previous glaciations was a major factor.

In the southern districts of Hertfordshire there may even have been a sea incursion, during a period when the ice retreated, and there were certainly cold Arctic environmental (periglacial) conditions across southern Britain at this time. This led to the deposition of windblown material, which is now detectable in the soils. These windblown deposits have in the past been used for brick-making; hence the often-used description of these as 'brickearths'. There is a classic site of these brickearth deposits at Caddington, south-west of Luton and nearby at Kinbourne Green and Gaddesdon Row. The importance of brick-making in this area is illustrated by the extensive brick manor house at Someries Castle, which was constructed in 1450, one of the earliest brick buildings in England.

Brickearths and Caddington Blues

The Bedfordshire brick-making tradition is usually associated with the imposing smoke stacks of Marston Vale, where the special properties of the Oxford Clay were utilised to make the high-quality London Bricks. However, there were many other brickworks which used a variety of geological materials. For example, the brick-making plants around Arlesey utilised the Gault Clays. There was also a specialist brick-making operation based at Caddington, south of Luton, which used a less common raw material known as brickearth. This fine-grained material is a relic of the last glaciation when wind-borne dust and silt formed as a fine rock flour was deposited across the landscape. Brickearth requires little or no admixture of other materials to render it suitable for the manufacture of 'stock bricks'. These wind-blown materials are characterised by a very uniform particle size and are common in France, where they take their scientific name of 'loess', from a town in the Alsace. Loess reaches its greatest extent in China. The finished brick product gives a range of distinctive colours after baking, and a 'Caddington Blue' was a well-known high-quality product known as an engineering brick, used in the lining of furnaces. Specific sites within the Caddington locality have also been credited with producing 'Greys', a common name for the plum-coloured brick produced from the flinty brickearths. To avoid confusion, the Caddington Blues are also a Morris-dancing side from the area!

As described above, clay soils with flint nodules are the most common and characteristic feature of this landscape, which continues southwards into Hertfordshire. Here the world-renowned Rothamsted Research Agricultural Institute is located south of Harpenden on this topography and for years scientists have studied and learned how to manage these soils. Opened in 1843 by John Lawes, this research facility is the oldest in the world and long-term trials provide an insight into how this land reacts to modern methods of cultivation. Farmers on these extensive arable lands have understood that, if cultivated when too wet, the fine and silty topsoil is easily damaged and yields of subsequent crops are reduced. In general, despite being over chalk, these soils are seasonally wet and generally acid, benefiting from added lime. These gentle slopes are well-wooded, especially in the west, where the Chiltern beech woods are famous and support (or did in the past) the furniture industry of places such as High Wycombe.

Both the Chiltern and Hertfordshire long-distance footpaths cross this country and provide a good insight into the landscape. In winter these footways can be very muddy with sticky clay. The Ashridge National Trust site, with its extensive beech woods across the Hertfordshire border, is typical of these Chiltern woods, which thrive on these soils. The old spelling of 'Asherugge', meaning a hill set with ash trees, suggests that ash was once predominant, although the area has since become better known for some of the finest examples of pollarded beech trees in Europe.

The Icknield Loam Belt

Looking north across the marl county towards Pulloxhill water tower

From the chalk hills, such as south of Barton, there are the most striking views across the clay vales to the north and west. There is also an area of gently sloping land very typical of Bedfordshire, sandwiched between the steep chalk scarp and the flat clay plains north of the Chilterns, around Luton. Drainage is usually difficult on these soils, which have dark grey and sometimes dull olive topsoil colours, obvious in the fields after ploughing, which can also turn up the chalk subsoils with clear white patches in many fields. A spring line is often present where the permeable chalk rocks meet the less permeable marl rocks at the foot of the escarpment, and this adds to the waterlogging and makes the area difficult to farm. Villages such as Barton and Edlesborough are located on this narrow belt of country, with the Middle Chalk scarp to the south and the Gault Clays to the north. The strip from Barton-le-Clay to Pirton and the area immediately north of Sharpenhoe are the best locations for this rather narrow transitional belt of country: south of Totternhoe in the vicinity of Eaton Bray is also typical.

The geology is often described as 'marl', which is difficult to describe exactly but is generally understood to be a soft rock with fine particles, often of silt size. The soils are always highly calcareous and the land is valued for wheat growing. The Lower Chalk is very different from the Middle and Upper formations, being very rich in clay, which suggests this rock was laid down in shallow seas close to a land mass that was being eroded.

The main influence on the topography and soils has been the presence of glacial ice which led to Arctic-like conditions ('periglacial'[3]), allowing permanently frozen subsoils and the movement of soil material from higher ground during the glacial epochs. This roughly sorted material is usually now referred to as 'head', which in this case is derived from the nearby chalk. The quarry workings within Totternhoe village extracted what is locally called 'clunch', which is a harder band of limestone, described by the quarry company as 'as ideal for artists, sculptures and landscape gardens'. This stone was used in the Swan Hotel in Bedford and more locally in Edlesborough Church.'

As this area is a transition between the clay flats of the Gault Clays and the steep downland of the Middle and Upper Chalk, the topography varies with the presence of local stream lines and is rarely more than gently sloping and crossed by streams rising from the scarp foot springs at the base of the Middle Chalk. The main feature of these soils is their calcareous nature, which is as expected, with the close proximity of the chalk upland and the deposits moving downslope during previous glacial periods. These soils are often wet, with occasionally flooding in winter, and are heavy clays or silts that are difficult to work and manage for arable agriculture.

Pasture land is common, and the proximity of large urban centres such as Luton has encouraged fields to be subdivided into paddocks for horses, which has become an important business. Cereals such as winter wheat,

---

(3)Periglacial – literally, 'around the glacier'. This term is used to describe a region adjacent to any ice sheet. These areas would have temporary snow caps and permafrost when ice was present.

with rotations of oilseed rape and barley, are common on this land, although it needs careful timing for field operations such as sowing or cultivation. This land is recognised as difficult to manage, but rewarding, being very fertile if treated with respect and given some luck with the weather.

The Man Orchid (Orchis anthropophora) *as found on the Bedfordshire chalk*

CHAPTER 4

THE CLAY VALES OF MID-BEDFORDSHIRE

If the chalk hills in the south of the county are the most dramatic of landscapes in Bedfordshire, then the clay lands, which cross the centre of Bedfordshire from south-west to north-east, are perhaps the most characteristic. The industrial landscapes, marked by the surviving smoke stacks of the Marston Vale brickworks (which extracted the Oxford Clay) are recognised by many who simply hurry across Bedfordshire on the motorway or the East Midland rail link. Adjacent to the steep chalk scarp described earlier, and the mid Bedfordshire ridge formed from the Greensand, is the belt of Gault Clay, stretching from Leighton Buzzard in the west, north of Barton, and eastwards to Wimpole Hall.

This ill-drained landscape is mirrored in the more extensive belt north of the Greensand Ridge formed of Oxford Clay. Modern systems of tiled and open field drainage, and the use of powerful farm machinery, have made both these clay belts productive arable land, and the scars of Marston Vale are rapidly being healed by the determined efforts of forestry, landscaping and recreation use. In this chapter we look first at the Gault Clay landscapes and their use and, second, at the Oxford Clays south of Bedford.

Clay Soil on the Gault Formation at Silsoe (Wicken Series)

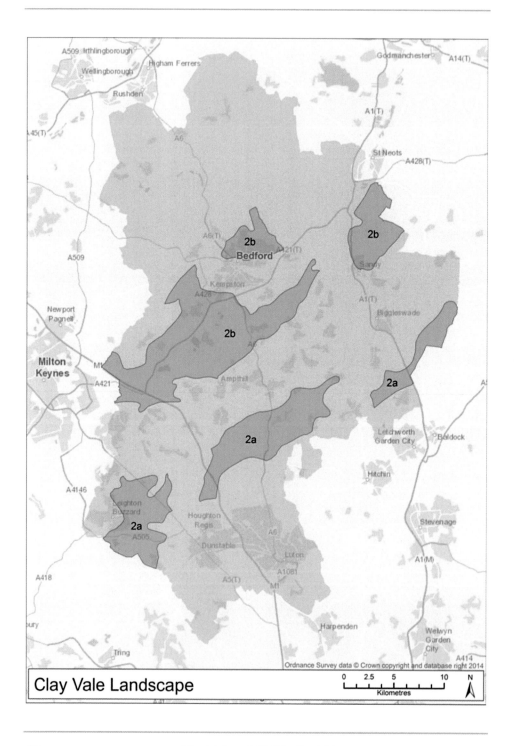

Clay Vale Landscape

Ordnance Survey data © Crown copyright and database right 2014

0   2.5   5   10
Kilometres
N

The Gault Clay Lands

This area north of the chalk scarp is not extensive but is one of the important clay vales that characterise the county of Bedfordshire. Looking north from the edge of the chalk, the land falls away to the clay plain, which stretches from near Harlington to the River Ivel, and eastward beyond the river in a narrow band all the way to Wimpole Hall on the Cambridgeshire border. This is difficult land to farm, but produces good cereal crops if the timing of cultivations can be carefully timed to avoid working a sodden soil. Farmers therefore choose winter-sown wheat as a favourite crop, with break crops of oilseed rape and sometimes beans. In 1943, when the land use of the whole of England was recorded by an army of volunteers, the Gault Clay vale was clearly distinguished as a 'farming type'. The description records 'heavy wet loams and clays which make permanent grassland the rule, and arable fields are few and scattered'.

A Splash of Colour or a Yellow Peril? Oilseed Rape Cropping in England

The vibrant yellow spring colour of oilseed crops in the landscape can either be viewed as a welcome splash of colour or an intrusion of Day-Glo into the tranquil green of English fields: many people are suspicious of this seemingly alien seed crop with the powerful scent. In the UK it is still regarded as a new crop, but has in fact been grown commercially in Europe since the thirteenth century. The rape plants are part of the brassica family and therefore related to the familiar turnip, mustard and cabbage: the cultivated variety is often known as 'canola', especially in North America. In England it has value as a 'break crop', a crop used to improve the yield of the following year's cereals: in Bedfordshire this is especially useful in combination with wheat. Oilseed rape is therefore grown as part of a farm rotation, with other break crops such as peas and field beans and sometimes potatoes.

During the 1970s there was an explosion in the area used for oilseed rape in the UK in response to increased commodity prices and targeted support from the European Union. Today it is the third most common arable crop in the UK, utilising around 12 per cent of the arable area. New varieties now provide oil that is suitable for cooking and use in food processing, and it has recently become an important component in biodiesel. Rapeseed produces lots of nectar and honeybees close to rape fields produce a light-coloured but peppery honey, which is usually blended for table use or sold for use in the confectionery trade.

The Gault Clay is ofCretaceous age, calcareous and slowly permeable. This thick sequence of bluish-grey clay was deposited in deep open water conditions and contains abundant marine fossils such as ammonites. The soil reflects this clay-rich geology and the land is therefore prone to waterlogging; the flat topography does not improve the drainage. Typical Gault is described as 'dark grey, stiff and tenacious'. This clay land also supported brick-building industries at Harlington and at Arlesey; these pits are now closed.

To understand how flat this landscape can be, follow the River Cam (also known as the Rhee) east from the village of Hixworth, north of Baldock. This is an area where large cereal fields are the norm, with only the chalk scarp to the south-east to provide any perspective. In the centre of the county there is a wedge of Gault Clay stretching from Harlington to Meppershall, with views to the north of the Greensand Ridge and to the south of the chalk scarp. The Soil Survey described this area as poorly-drained clays, which are seasonally waterlogged and require skilful management. The critical feature of these soils is waterlogging in winter. From late November to early April, cultivation and access for farm machinery on these areas is not recommended. There are, however, usually sufficient days in autumn for satisfactory cultivation, and these fields are suited to direct drilling with minimum cultivation. Farmers find it advantageous to carry out deeper cultivations periodically to break up any plough pans due to compaction. The importance of timing cultivations on these soils was well understood long before the advent of heavy machinery. A sixteenth-century Husbandry Guide recommended:

> 'Go upon the lande that is plowed and if it synge or crye or
> make any noyse under thy fete it is too wet to sow. If it
> make no noyse and will beare thy horses, thane sowe in
> the name of God.'

The advances in farm machinery, drainage and careful tillage have established the current trend toward a landscape dominated by arable crops such as wheat and oilseed rape. An early soil survey of the Silsoe Estate, which is mostly located on these clays, was undertaken in 1945. The survey map traced a boundary between the better-drained soils on the edge of the Greensand to the north and the dark and ill-drained clays to the south. The surveyor noted on his field sheet that 'the grey calcareous clays are probably undisturbed Gault', which is an accurate description of the geology.

The land to the south of the access road to Wrest Park House at Silsoe, which was once used as an experimental field by the National Institute of

Agricultural Engineering, is also typical of this Gault Clay. The complex drainage systems within Wrest Park gardens are evidence not only of the skills of the landscape gardener, but also the difficulty of draining these flat clay fields. The parishes of Battlesden and Potsgrove in the west of the county are also typical of these clay areas. In the east there are good walks around Wimpole Hall, but these paths can be very wet from November to well into the spring.

The Oxford Clay Vale

The brick chimneys of Stewartby are perhaps the best-known landmark in the county, visible from the motorway and rail routes into the Midlands. These mark the site of one of Bedfordshire's greatest industries, which was based on the brick-making characteristics of the Oxford Clay. The brick pits subsequently became a valued resource for the dumping of London's rubbish, and the landscape is now undergoing another transformation with the planning of millions of trees in the Marston Vale Forest. More recently, the use of the old brick pits for water sports, the proposal to site wind turbines adjacent to the landfill areas, and the planning of new housing will again transform the exceptionally flat landscape. Just how flat this landscape can be is best seen in the areas once known as the Bedfordshire Fens, north of Wilstead and south of Elstow. The topographic map here is free of any contours, and deep open ditches cross the arable fields. The agricultural use of this land was made possible by the extensive under-field drainage carried out in the nineteenth century to allow the cultivation of the broad cereal fields which now surround the residue of the brick-makers. This is the landscape of John Bunyan's 'slough of despond', which he had to cross to climb to the 'house beautiful' on the Greensand Ridge beyond. The trials of Bunyan tramping across this land reflect the difficult, ill-drained nature of this topography before it was drained.

The usual description of this important geological deposit, the Oxford Clay, is a greenish or bluish-grey shaly mudstone of Jurassic age. The work of the geologists employed by the London Brick Company has refined this and there are a number of academic studies which describe the variations in the Oxford clay zones. There is general agreement that there is up to 600 feet of this deposit, which is present along a diagonal tract across England from Weymouth in Dorset to Scarborough in Yorkshire. The most common variation in the clays are the Kellaway Beds, which are a sandy series of strata at the junction with the Oxford Clay and the rocks below.

The substantial brick-making industry developed on Oxford Clays produced the Fletton brick, which is easily pressed into shape and, more importantly, the high proportion of combustible material in the clay accelerates the firing process. Estimated at up to 5 per cent carbon, this ignited and resulted in substantial savings in the fuel required by the kilns; therefore the process of firing Fletton bricks in continuous kilns was possible with a minimum of fuel being used. The 1970s proposal that low-level radioactive waste should be stored in the Elstow area, which was subsequently abandoned after public protest, was based on the stability and uniformity of these deposits, which at this point are some 50 feet above the Kellaway Beds.

***Looking north from the Greensand Ridge to Bedford and the
brickworks on Oxford Clay***

This landscape has in the past been seen as the least attractive in the county, and the reclamation of the Marston Vale was seen as a priority. The giant brick pits are now being filled and used for recreation and as nature reserves, making the Marston Vale a valuable resource. The Vale is now perceived as a valuable resource with potential for housing, retail distribution centres, sustainable energy generation and recreation on brownfield sites.

However, this modern landscape must be vastly different from the views as experienced before drainage or the arrival of the brick-makers. A description of the Oxford Clay from elsewhere in the country paints a dismal picture: the clays as described as 'giving rise to heavy sodden soils and the landscape is featureless. There are few good roads and in the eighteenth century oxen were used to pull coaches in some parts as horses could not move in the stiff clay'. This would all be familiar to Bunyan.

From Fens to Field: Draining the Clays

While Bedfordshire has not seen the dramatic drainage of fenland which has shaped the eastern counties of East Anglia, the drainage of land has been undertaken for many centuries in the county, and has influenced the land use, agricultural practices, wildlife and landscapes that we see today. A peak of field drainage activity was reached in the latter half of the nineteenth century, when 12 million acres across Britain were drained from 1840 to 1890. Some drainage schemes were large-scale and dramatic, such as the drainage of the Cambridgeshire Fens in the seventeenth century, but others are small-scale and may have only affected an individual field. In Bedfordshire the land south of Elstow is the only example of this large-scale drainage operation using open drains, and the John Bunyan Trail, south of Medbury Farm, crosses this distinctive landscape. These improvements allowed modern or intensive methods of agricultural production to be undertaken, and the mainte- nance of these drainage systems is often required to support arable production today. It is estimated that some 70 per cent of Bedfordshire has a clay subsoil and almost all of this will have benefited from sub- surface drainage in some form. Drainage improvement was part of a package of updated agricultural practices and road transport that swept the country during the later eighteenth and early nineteenth century. The introduction of land drainage in more poorly drained low-lying areas, the improvement of agricultural implements, the introduction of mechanisa- tion and the introduction of new breeds of sheep and cattle all contribut- ed to agricultural development in the nineteenth century. Other innovations in this period included the adoption of new crop rotations to improve soil fertility, the addition of lime or marl to improve soil tilth, the growing of root crops such as turnips to assist in the overwintering of livestock, and the introduction of potatoes as part of the human staple diet, which here – as elsewhere – helped to sustain small-scale subsist- ence agriculture in more marginal areas.

The soils of the Vale are the classic clays, with signs of impeded drainage close to the surface dominated by wet clays, which are free of stones, and waterlogged for long periods in winter. The overburden from the brick-making, known in the industry as 'callow', is especially difficult to plant and presently supports only hawthorn shrubs close to the pits. There is little opportunity for the working of the land in spring, so autumn-sown crops are favoured. Because the surface soils take a long time to dry, the timing of cultivations is critical. Farmers here have adapted by the use of specialist modern direct drill machinery but, even in autumn, caution is required. If the land is wet there is a danger that machinery will damage the topsoil, leading to a compacted layer, resulting in poor germination, and when conditions are too dry the soil is too hard for good penetration of a drill. With livestock the problems are also severe: soils 'poach', or puddle, leading to muddy fields and damage to the topsoil. Thanks to the work of the mainly Irish drainers of the nineteenth century these lands are now intensively under-drained with tiles and can – with care – produce good cereal crops. The Marston Vale Forest Park provides a view of the brick-working, the reclamation works and the adjacent agricultural arable land.

The Bedfordshire Fens: an area reclaimed by deep drainage ditches north of Wilstead

CHAPTER 5

THE GREENSAND RIDGE

The landscape of mid Bedfordshire is given its special character by the distinctive Greensand Ridge of higher land which transverses the county from the north-east at Sandy to the south-west at Leighton Buzzard. The Ridge is at no point very high and is certainly never a barrier to communications, but it does provide an abrupt separation between the clay vales to the north and south, and has in the past been a dry route-way, above these ill-drained clays. The characteristic geology, with warm brown flaky sandstone, can be seen in many of the parish churches in the county. The presence of steep-sided dry valleys incised into the Ridge, and the sandy, acid soils, have discouraged agriculture, leaving the Ridge for settlements, woods, grazing land, parkland and present-day recreation facilities such as golf courses and a mountain biking trail.

Recreation use along the Greensand Ridge in Aspley Wood

The Ridge in some places is, however, thinly covered in a layer of glacial boulder clay (or 'till'), which results in smoother contours and wetter, but deeper, soils which occasionally still support relic woodland. The long-distance Greensand Ridge footpath allows access to the attractive scenery along this spine of the county, with many views south to the chalk, and north to the Ouse floodplain and beyond. Many of the most popular recreation areas in the county benefit from the Greensand geology, including Ampthill and Rushmere Country Parks, the Woburn Estate and the heaths at Aspley and Sandy.

Bedfordshire as a county is usually perceived – and portrayed – as flat. The wet clay lands of the Barton Vale and the Oxford Clays south of Bedford are certainly both flat and wet in winter, as are the clays derived from the glacial deposits which have left a veneer of clays over the upland areas north of Bedford. However, at the heart of the county the Greensand Ridge rises up from these difficult clay lands to form a dry and airy corridor of loamy and sandy soils across almost the whole of Bedfordshire, stretching from near Leighton Buzzard to the similar landscape around Sandy Warren.

Much of the Greensand belt has always been marginal for cultivation and included large areas of common land before enclosure. Accounts of the progress of enclosure dating from around 1800 remark on the extent of unenclosed land in Bedfordshire, in comparison to neighbouring counties. Much of this was described as 'waste' – more likely, this was the infertile sandy soils along the Greensand Ridge. Today the importance of this Ridge to those who live in the county is marked by the Greensand Ridge Walk, which loops across the county from south-west to north-east, providing great walking and views of the lower clay land to both north and south. For more details of the Greensand Ridge long-distance path, see Chapter 10.

Green Rocks and Silver Sand

The Greensand Ridge is formed from an outcrop of Lower Greensand which is now referred to by geologists in Bedfordshire as the Woburn Sands Formation, and which stretches from Ely to Leighton Buzzard. These rocks are dated to the Lower Cretaceous period and were laid down in a narrow sea lane from the Wash, across Bedfordshire, and beyond to the Isle of Wight.

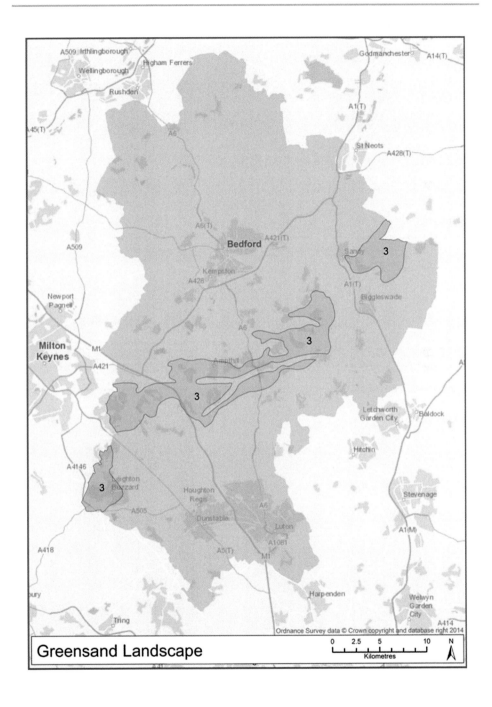

Greensand Landscape

The rocks included within the Woburn Sands Formation are highly variable and range from resistant tabular masses of sandstone to consolidated sands. 'Green' is something of a misnomer, as exposures range from yellow to rusty-red, reflecting the high concentration of iron within these sediments which oxidises to produce the characteristic red colouration. Where it is possible to examine freshly exposed sections, it may have a greenish tinge due to the presence of a mineral called glauconite. The building stones used for the church tower at Husborne Crawley is perhaps the best example of a truly green Greensand.

The term mostly associated with these rocks in Bedfordshire is 'ferruginous sands'. Exposures of the Lower Greensand can best be seen at the Tiddenfoot and Ledburn quarries, close to Leighton Buzzard, both of which are now open to the public. These quarries were worked for sand until the 1960s, and have now been restored to create a recreational area for both people and wildlife.

Looking carefully at the quarry walls, it is still possible to see the layering or cross-stratification of these sands as they were laid down below the sea, much like a modern beach. These deposits were the pure and valuable silver sands, and elsewhere within the Lower Greensand there are quarries extracting Fuller's Earth – a much sought-after mineral which is present in pockets within the Greensand and has been mined since Roman times.

Walkers enjoy good access to the forestry land in many parts of the Greensand

Mining the Greensand: Fertiliser and Fossils

The Woburn Sands Formation sediments were also important to the early agricultural industry in England with the valuable production of fertiliser from the phosphatic nodules, which remain in hollows within the underlying Gault Clay. This formation is described by geologists as the Cambridge Greensand, which is a thin irregular bed of calcareous clay, together with a very mixed collection of other rocks washed into the area. County records reveal that many people were employed in the digging of what were then described as coprolites (fossilised faecal pellets of fish, reptiles, birds or mammals which are high in phosphate, hence their use as a fertiliser). The industry reached its peak between 1840 and 1870 and only ended when the fossil-bearing seams became too deep to access and refined phosphate fertiliser was imported from the USA. There was a revival during the First World War but the government project was closed in 1919. The novelty of this industry has led to headlines such as 'Lost Industry Based on Dinosaur Dung', but in fact all fossil bones are high in phosphate, which is an essential nutrient for plant growth. By 1871, it is recorded that 375 people were listed as coprolite diggers in the county. Coprolites were big business: once washed and sorted across thousands of acres along the junction of the Gault Clay with the Greensand, the fertiliser was in demand across England. As a sideline, diggers would pocket the best fossils to supply the ready market in fossil collecting, which was a nineteenth-century hobby enjoyed by the upper classes. This was a time of increased income for both the landowners and the miners, and early accounts note the abundance of pubs close to these workings. The 'dung rush' came to a close with cleaner imported fertiliser around the beginning of the twentieth century.

The Greensand Ridge Path offers a great introduction to the topography of this landscape. The steep north-facing scarp, well developed in Ampthill Great Park for example, provides views across the Oxford Clay plain to the north. A spring line at the base of these hills marks the junction of the permeable sandstone and the impervious clays below. Where the exposures of Greensand are at their best, there is little doubt about the geology – the Sandy Warren close to the Royal Society for the Protection of Birds (RSPB) headquarters at Sandy; the heath land of Cooper's Hill Site of Special Scientific Interest (SSSI) close to Ampthill; and the expansive grounds of Woburn Abbey are all typical of this topography. The word 'warren' is common along the Ridge, indicating the presence of rabbits, as at Warden Warren, used by the monks of Warden Abbey as a food source. This reflects the rabbits' ease of burrowing in these less compact subsoils.

Elsewhere, the picture is more complicated, with often a thin cover of the ice-deposited till or boulder clay softening the landscape and turning the underfoot conditions from the sands to a sticky clay. A good example of this is at the SSSI close to Maulden Church. The church meadow has acid soils on the Greenland close to the church but, just a little to the north, and also within the SSSI, the boulder clay capping gives a much more calcareous soil with a different community of grassland vegetation. A walk over the fields north of Maulden, especially in the winter, can collect significant mud on one's boots crossing the boulder clay. However, there is more pleasant and easier walking on the sandy Greensand geology close to the village.

This veneer of till is important for the agriculture on the Ridge and this was recognised as early as 1808. An important agricultural survey of the county published in that year notes that 'this sandy belt mostly presents a hilly surface with clays and various loams in the intervening vales and sometimes clay on the tops of the hills'. An excellent example of this is at Maulden Wood, which is partly on a clay plateau and therefore wet. Generally across the Greensand belt, the woodland on the slopes is secondary and in the past land has been cleared for farming and then replanted with conifers, such as at Aspley Heath. These sandy soils have limited agricultural use due to low fertility and uneven topography. One of the pioneers of agricultural improvement, John Morton, writing about Bedfordshire in 1838,[4] noted that 'the black and white silvery sands are the worst soils and naturally produce nothing but heath of low natural fertility, and the natural habitat would be dry pasture, and lowland heath'. The characteristic natural vegetation would be heather (*Calluna vulgaris*) or bilberries (*Vaccinium myrtillus*). These plants produce a coarse litter of stems and leaves which is difficult to break down and incorporate in the topsoil. This then often forms a black organic layer – hence John Morton's comment on black soils.

The properties of these sandy soils has meant that a more appropriate use for the land was for forestry and grazing. Just before the Black Death arrived, a taxation return for around 1340 noted that in Potton the villagers declared, 'the land is sandy and of little value in a dry year'. Likewise, at Ridgmont, 'the soils were sandy for the greater part and produce nothing except rye'.

Technically, the soils are classified as freely drained sandy-brown earths, for the most part with a rather rare occurrence (for southern England) of a

---

(4) John Morton walked most of the counties of England and Scotland in the early nineteenth century and published a book in 1838, *On the Nature and Property of Soils: Their connection to the geological formation on which they rest; the best means of permanently increasing their productiveness and on the rents and profits of agriculture.*

soil described as a *podzol* (5)– a very leached sandy soil with an ash-like white layer – which occurs at Apsley Heath. All these soils need phosphate fertilisers, and there are many deficiencies in mineral nutrients such as copper; the acid nature of the soil also means that liming is necessary. However, the favourable light loams have historically been used for the cultivation of intensive horticultural crops, if irrigation water can be supplied. One of the characteristics of these soils is that the surface soil breaks down in heavy rain, and forms a 'cap', which restricts the emergence of seedlings. Local farmers would say the soil 'goes sad', which is a colourful way of describing the lack of any friable topsoil.

The marginal nature of this land is evident from the historical record and the current use by landowners. Golf courses are common and Millbrook can be played when the Wavendon course on clays is trickier in winter. The championship course at Woburn is a classic example of Greensand topography. The Forestry Commission has invested in pine plantations, as have private owners, with an explosion in planting just after the Second World War. More recently, Pegnut Wood, just south of Potton, was planted in the 1990s with a species of poplar tree, which yields timber used in packing boxes for food items and coffins.

Ancient maps show this area as 'pignut wood', referring to the use of the area by pigs foraging for nuts and edible roots. Rowney Warren is now a nationally recognised mountain bike training ground, and Millbook has a site for testing the performance of off-road motor vehicles, which utilise the steep slopes of the landscape.

This is also the area of the great estates, such as Woburn, with often the house and grounds on upstanding drier land, with the more profitable and farmed cereal land on the clay belts. There is the attractive Sutton Park, owned by the historic Burgoyne family, for example, and the pleasant landscapes surrounding Old Warden and Southill villages. An unusual land use is the Warden Abbey vineyard at Southill Park. Producing around 14,000 bottles per year, this site is close to the ancient Cistercian Abbey vineyard which was founded in the twelfth century and was abandoned following the Dissolution of the Monasteries in 1538. Replanted in 1986, the vineyard now produces high-quality whites from Rhineland grape varieties such as Müller-Thurgau and Reichensteiner.

---

(5) The word *podzol* comes from Russian, meaning *an ash soil*. The ash refers to the bleached grey or white colouration in the layer or horizon just below the surface where all colour, nutrients and clay have been leached out.

The Clay that Cleans: Fuller's Earth in Bedfordshire

The Lower Greensand geology which forms such a striking landscape feature across the county has provided easily quarried building stone, high-quality sand, and a less well-known resource in the form of very fine clay known as Fuller's Earth. This is an uncommon mineral and is formed from altered volcanic ash which has, over time, become an exceptionally fine-grained clay. In the Bedfordshire Greensand the clay is at the optimum depth for mining; if it is buried deeper, the alteration process continues, the value of the clay decreases, and the cost of extraction rises. The significance of this clay is that it is formed from extremely fine particles, which means that a given amount of clay has a very large surface area: this enables these particles to have an electrical charge that attracts and binds other molecules. When freshly extracted, Fuller's Earth feels slippery and soap-like, and this feature probably led to its early use as a cleaning agent. Certainly by the thirteenth century there are records of this clay being used to remove grease and oil from sheep fleeces, and by the end of the seventeenth century its export from England was banned, to conserve supplies for the woollen industry. Before this product became widely used, the Roman practice was to use urine for cleansing wool. In the eighteenth century the Duke of Bedford began commercial mining around Wavendon, and by the 1890s there was a thriving trade with the Yorkshire woollen industry. Other quarries were at Clophill and Apsley Heath. While this product has found a host of new uses in oil well drilling, paper manufacture, cosmetics and even in cat litter, it is no longer mined in Bedfordshire.

Cooper's Hill SSSI west of Ampthill is a classic example of lowland heath in southern England, with heather the dominant vegetation. This site is managed by the Bedfordshire, Cambridgeshire and Northamptonshire Wildlife Trust on behalf of Ampthill Town Council. In the past few years it has undergone a programme of rehabilitation to clear intrusive vegetation, such as bracken, and allow the natural heath land to flourish. Lowland heath is one of the most threatened habitats in the country and this site represents an important relic.

Another important site is the Sandy Warren reserve managed by the RSPB to encourage a range of bird species, and which encourages visitors. Rushmere Country Park provides another access point.

Exposure in a Greensand sand quarry at Leighton Buzzard

CHAPTER 6

THE CLAY UPLANDS

As has been explained elsewhere in this book (see, for example, Chapter 11), Bedfordshire is a county which still has an agricultural heartland with arable agriculture dominant, especially in the clay vales. The centre and particularly the north of the county also have extensive belts of upland clay subsoils, described geologically as 'chalky boulder clay'.

The North Bedfordshire Uplands: wide field margins or headland left for environmental reasons

These clays are glacial in origin, and the material deposited during this period covers higher land which is often bleak and exposed. The value of this land for farming, however, has never been doubted and this was recognised in the early enclosures, which have left a distinct imprint on the landscapes in north Bedfordshire. In the middle of the county the Greensand Ridge is also covered in many places by a veneer of glacial drift, but this is less chalky and derived from the underlying sandstones. In this chapter the area north of the River Ouse has been described as the North Beds uplands.

Chalky boulder clays, north Bedfordshire

William Camden, who produced the first topographic description of the British Isles around 1600, visited Bedfordshire and described the county as divided into two parts by the River Ouse. North of the river is 'the more fruitfull of the twaine and the more woody'. This northern clay upland is certainly the most extensive landscape in the county, reaching from the edge of the Ouse terraces into north Bedfordshire and beyond into Northamptonshire. There is, for example, a distinct step at the edge of the Ouse terraces as the road to the north climbs past Mowsbury Park towards Cleat Hill and then Sunderland Hill towards Kimbolton.

In this area the influence of the Parliamentary enclosures in the eighteenth and nineteenth centuries is evident: minor roads often have wide verges bounded by hawthorn hedges with regularly spaced large trees, usually ash or elm, in the hedgerow. Roads and farm tracks enclosing roughly rectangular fields may have sudden right-angled bends, and the landscape is dotted with wooded spinneys, reflecting the importance of this country for hunting. Other woodland can be more ancient – often hanger woods [6] on hillsides survived the medieval clearance for agriculture. Typical of these wooded areas are deciduous species such as oak and ash, with rowan, hornbeam and aspen; these woodlands are often rich with bluebells in the spring.

The Geological Survey map sheet for Bedford (number 203) has a uniform grey tone which is described as 'glacial boulder clay'. In north Bedfordshire this overlies the Jurassic Oxford Clay and, in the middle of the county, the characteristic sticky clay overlies the Greensand. These are the uplands of Bedfordshire, with wide views and exposed landscapes. Trees are sparse, and winter temperatures are a few degrees colder than lower ground, with wind chill especially north of Bedford. The heavy clay soils make this a cold area which farmers need to manage carefully, especially when planning machinery work on wet soils, to avoid soil compaction. Winter-sown crops are preferred, as working of the land takes place in the autumn or immediately after harvest, when ground conditions are usually favourable.

---

(6) A hanger woodland is a residual wood which clings to a steep slope, often in a narrow valley. Woods such as these survive because the land is not worth clearing for farmland, due to its steep slope.

The figure below illustrates how these soils dominate the landscape of the county and influence wild plant distribution. *Silaum silaus,* pepper saxifrage, is a good indicator of these soils, preferring damp and unimproved grassland as a habitat. The main characteristic of this land is the sticky and tenacious nature of the glacially deposited boulder clay or till, which is the material in which these clay soils form. The early maps carefully distinguish soils that are calcareous and those which, have over time, lost the calcium in the top half-metre and are said to be decalcified. This chalk influence derives from calcareous material picked up by ice from the floor of the North Sea far to the north-east. This feature is important for agriculture, as the presence of calcium helps to give the soil some structure and tilth, which assists with water penetration and makes the soils less wet in winter. Farming these soils is less arduous than in the clay vales formed within the Oxford and Gault Clays.

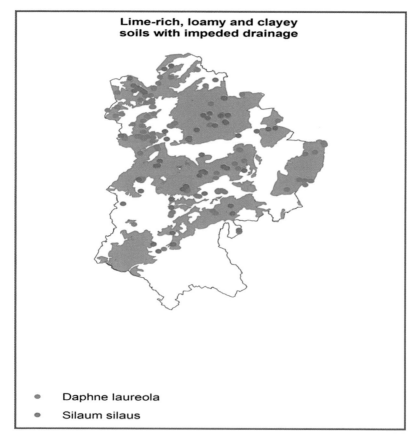

Lime-rich, loamy and clayey soils with impeded drainage

- ● Daphne laureola
- ● Silaum silaus

Distribution of clay soils in Bedfordshire (CA Boon and AR Outen)

Much of the landscape we see today dates from the period when the open fields cultivated in strips by medieval farmers were enclosed, leaving the unmistakable pattern of ridge and furrow as the only relic of a former agricultural landscape. By the end of the seventeenth century, there was a trend in the Midlands of England to replace tillage by grass, especially on heavy clay lands where sheep replaced the corn of the medieval peasant. As mentioned in Chapter 1, the eviction of the open field peasants was not seen as a problem, once Parliament had passed the necessary legislation.

However, this phase of enclosure was slow and in 1750 much of Bedfordshire was still open fields. Within a hundred years, the landscape we are familiar with today, of neat fields and hedges, had replaced the open field pattern. Enclosure allowed more livestock farming, then seen as profitable, but today these clay lands have reverted to arable production of cereals with break crops of oilseed rape and beans (see Chapter 1).

Much of the new tree planting undertaken by the Marston Vale Forest is on these soils as the park expands eastwards towards Cranfield. The wood at Marston Thrift is an example. To experience a landscape where the enclosures are evident, look north of the A422 around Stagsden, where there is a dense network of well-marked footpaths.

North Bedfordshire: use of woodland for ecologically friendly burial plots

The Mid Bedfordshire Hills

The landscape character of mid Bedfordshire is often thought of as being defined by the Greensand Ridge, with the long-distance footpath linking woods and heath and giving views of the clay vales to both south and north. South of the Ridge, the glacial history of the area has resulted in a number of 'islands' covered by a thickness of clay or glacial drift which produces a landscape of gentle hills, usually in arable production of wheat or oil seed rape.

The land east of Haynes or around Pulloxhill is typical of this area, which is similar to the more extensive upland till landscapes of north Bedfordshire described above. The difference lies mostly in elevation, with the mid Beds hill land a little lower and less exposed to wind; the landscape reflects this more gentle character. In the east of the county there is a long ridge of this glacial till which grades into the Ivel terraces close to Biggleswade but becomes more distinctive in the wooded area around Cockayne Hatley.

In the middle of the county, glacial deposits with the characteristic sticky clay overlie the Greensand. In Bedfordshire generally, only the highest landscape points are free from glacial deposits, as the Anglian ice sheet flowed around them. These account for the change in character of the Greensand Ridge footpath, for example, as it transverses the dry, sandy heaths of Ampthill and Sandy but crosses the till or boulder clay deposits around Haynes. A good example of the transition from the Greensand to land with a boulder clay capping is at King's Wood near Houghton House, Ampthill.

The essential feature of these mid Bedfordshire landscapes is smooth hills which are often wooded, and a characteristic man-made marker is the presence of water towers such as at Pulloxhill. Woodland is common and now valued as cover for shooting, and often protected by some form of conservation scheme: the experimental coppicing of woods at Moggerhanger is one example. Soils are always imperfectly or poorly drained and have a subsoil of clay which is calcareous. The fact that these soils do have some chalk influence helps to improve the structure of the topsoil and makes the drainage less of a problem, but, as mentioned before, the timing of cultivation in the autumn needs skill and judgement as heavy machinery will compact the soil.

The use of this clay upland is dominated by arable farming with grain production reaching high yields across both mid and north Bedfordshire. Large farming enterprises are more frequent in this area, an example being the Bedfordia Group, which farms 2,200 hectares (5,000 acres) centred on

Milton Ernest. This group takes pride in its responsible approach to farming and land management, and is involved in the LEAF whole farm assurance scheme (which links the environment and farming), the Countryside Stewardship Scheme, and opens the farm to the public through farm open days. At the same time, yields of wheat in this enterprise exceed ten tonnes to the hectare (the 2013 average across England was just short of eight tonnes to the hectare).

A less commercial, community enterprise is the use of clay land north of Bedford to pioneer top fruit production. This area was once utilised by the Laxton family as a working orchard and fruit breeding nursery, and a community effort has attempted to revive this minor agricultural industry.

Old Crops and New Owners: Community Orchards

In 1997 an area adjacent to allotments in north Bedford was designated a Local Nature Reserve (LNR) by Bedford Borough Council and local residents have taken an active part in managing it. In I999 part of the area which was rough grassland was set aside for a new community orchard, intended to conserve local fruit varieties and benefit wildlife. It was decided to stock the orchard with fruit trees developed by the famous Laxton brothers, horticulturists who were based in Bedford from 1860 until 1957. Here they developed many award-winning fruits and Thomas Laxton (1830–93) even conducted experiments on hybridisation for Charles Darwin. Sadly, nothing remains of the Laxtons in Bedford apart from a few street names that were built on the nurseries themselves. The once great apple and pear varieties are now rarely heard of and are almost unobtainable. The new orchard has two specimens of all the Laxtons' apple trees and many of the pear varieties, including very old ones such as William Peddy. There are also figs, greengages, plums, damsons, mulberry, medlar, quince and walnuts. There are now 231 trees in the orchard, all taken from cuttings from the fruit tree collection at Brogdale Horticultural Trust in Kent. All the famous Laxton varieties are here including Laxton's Superb, Lord Lambourne and Laxton's Fortune. The fruit trees already look impressive, even though there are some problems with waterlogging in the winter and drying out in the summer, which is typical of these clay soils. The consolation is that we know it is the same Bedfordshire clay that the Laxtons had to deal with.

The Park Wood Local Nature Reserve and Community Orchard,

Bedford

CHAPTER 7

THE RIVER VALLEYS

Most people in Bedfordshire live on or close to the lowlands carved out by the major rivers that cross the county. The presence of these major lowland rivers is important in understanding how varied the landscape is within a relatively small English county. While the influence of the River Ouse in Bedford is very evident in shaping the character of the town, that of the River Lea, rising north of Luton then reappearing from under the town to the south, is at first not so obvious. The river, however, does benefit the city, providing flat land with easily worked gravels ideal for building.

The underlying character of the county is bound up with the river valleys or, more accurately, the valley deposits of sand and gravel. These have left a widespread relic landscape of extraction workings, together with the flat, easily workable loam soils which were the essential foundation for the market gardening industry. The river valleys are also important for unique landscapes such as the lowland peat deposits of the Flit moors, and water meadows close to the Ouse. This chapter therefore takes the River Ouse and its tributary the Ivel together, and then briefly notes the unique landscape of the Flit Vale, also discussing the flat lands bordering the Kym and its tributary the river Til, in north Bedfordshire.

The Ouse, Ivel and Hiz Valleys

The flat terraces of the River Ouse, together with its north-flowing tributary the Ivel and its tributary the Hiz (pronounced 'Hitch'), form one of the best-known areas of Bedfordshire, if only because they are very accessible from all the major population centres. These valleys also contain some of the best agricultural land in England, often classed as Grade 1 or 2, and are at the heart of the market garden industry for which the county was once famous.

These riverine areas have always formed the route-ways into the agricultural heartland of England and have been important for access and transport throughout history. Consequently they are important for archaeology, as is clear from the Neolithic remains in gravel workings, and the routes of Roman roads, which follow the river terraces. The former gravel workings, many of which have now been reclaimed, are not as intrusive in the landscape as the great brick-making pits of the Marston Vale, and in recent years the county has begun the task of healing the scars left by the extraction of sand and gravels along the Ouse, and converting them to amenity and recreational use.

The importance of the rivers for transporting agricultural produce in the past has left a network of paths where a kingfisher may still be glimpsed among the willows on the river bank, and otters are beginning to return. Country parks such as Priory Country Park in Bedford is – sometime in the future – to be complemented by regeneration of the land downstream in the proposed Bedford River Valley Park, which will provide enhanced opportunities for urban dwellers along the Bedfordshire rivers. The generally well-drained soils and the often billiard-table flatness of the landscape have attracted both agriculture and industry: the Priory Country Park, with its marina and links to the newly rehabilitated cycle route 51, are all examples of increasing leisure use in the Ouse Valley.

A former gravel pit at Felmersham is now a bird reserve

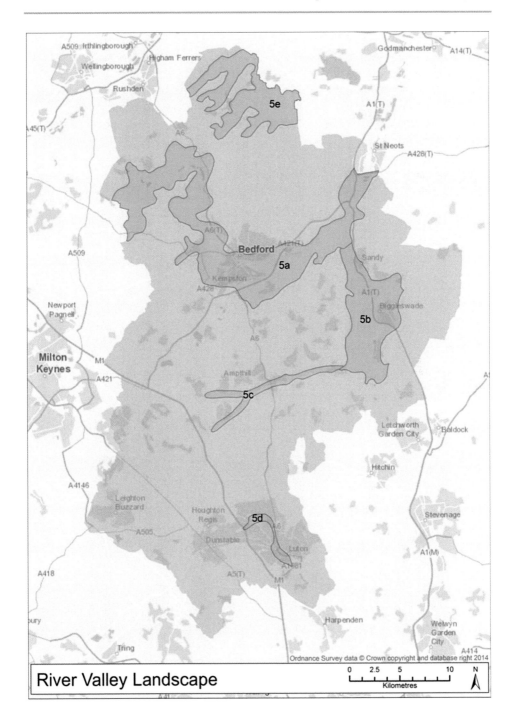

River Valley Landscape

Ordnance Survey data © Crown copyright and database right 2014

0   2.5   5   10   N
Kilometres

The alluvial terraces of the Ouse, Ivel and Hiz are formed in a variety of gravel beds of variable thickness. The older, and usually higher, terraces have a loamy surface soil which makes the drainage ideal for arable farming. Flat open landscapes with large fields are mixed with intimate views of the rivers, interspersed with small villages which hug the edge of the floodplain, hoping not to experience the 'once a century' floods to which the area is prone. The soils of the Biggleswade market garden area were studied in some detail by Cambridge-based scientist, Theodore Rigg, during the First World War, when the importance of this area was recognised for food production. He surveyed an area of around 100 square miles from Henlow to St Neots, on a north-to-south axis and from Willington to Gamlingay east to west.

The presence of market garden production extended well beyond the terraces of the rivers and in many areas reached the slopes of Lower Greensand where the sandy soils were made more productive by a thin veneer of clay-rich glacial till. All alluvial soils are variable and reflect the history of the rivers which created them. Therefore in the Ouse Valley the gravel subsoils are covered by a darker, more fertile, loam which was highly prized by the market gardeners in places such as Wyboston. Close to Biggleswade the rich, light loams reflect the land into which the rivers drain, leading to a fertile mix of materials from the Greensand, the chalk and the Gault Clays.

The combination of loams, which contain enough clay to be fertile, but with gravel at a depth which allows good drainage, is ideal and this good fortune is celebrated in the older Bedfordshire farming couplet: 'clay over sand is money in the hand'.

The gravels of the valley deposits may not always have been ideal for cropping, but their value for the construction industry cannot be overlooked. The newly widened and re-engineered A421 south, and then east, of Bedford sweeps from the Marston Vale with deep cuttings into the clays, onto the elevated sections across the gravels and river floodplains approaching Great Barford. County planners' aspiration is to convert these landscapes, formerly scarred by gravel extraction, into the Bedford River Valley Park. The development of recreational landscaped parks in old gravel workings has been a feature over the last decade, and access to the Priory Country Park and the Harrold-Odell Country Park is welcomed by many people. Bird watchers are welcome in these locations, which attract more winter wildfowl as the landscapes become more appealing. A less well-known nature reserve is on the old gravel workings north of Felmersham.

*Cattle grazing on reclaimed land in the Ouse Valley
close to Bedford*

Terraces are by definition flat, and are therefore ideal for building. Bedford is the best example and the occurrence of regular, severe floods which have swamped built-up areas close to the river are constant reminders of the dangers of building on floodplains. Significant and widespread flooding in 2012 and again in 2013 is a timely reminder that at the end of 2012 there were 28,000 outstanding applications to build homes on floodplains across England: it would seem there is still an appetite for waterside living, despite evidence of more regular inundations. Other non-agricultural use which values flat river terraces are the former airship industrial building at Cardington, whose giant hangars dominate the skyline, and the older airfield at Castle Mill east of Bedford. Less romantically, sewage works are the other valued use of these terraces and riverine alluvial strips.

Where flooding is regular or drainage imperfect, landowners have managed the land as rough grazing, which has become interesting wildlife habits. A sighting of an otter in the Ouse east of Bedford was reported in February 2014.

The importance of these river valleys for communication can be seen in many parts of the county. Views from the Iron Age forts within the RSPB reserve at Sandy are now obscured by recent coniferous plantations on the hill beneath the forts, but when the forts were constructed, they would have commanded good views across the valley. Galley Hill, sited on a prominent spur of land adjacent to the bird reserve, was confirmed an Iron Age structure by excavations in 2006.

Market garden crops in the Ouse Valley

The Upper Ouse Limestone Valley

North of Bedford, the sinuous loops of the River Ouse have exposed the solid geology, allowing this useful building stone to be quarried and resulting in attractive limestone villages such as Bromham, Pavenham and Felmersham. A common feature of these villages is that the settlement clings to the edge of the floodplain with often a multi-spanned limestone bridge approached by a bank or raised causeway. These bridges and the lower reaches of the villages are often still overcome by flooding, despite improvements in road and river alignments. The 20-arched bridge at Bromham is a classic example. A walk through Bromham Park leading to the pleasant limestone church of St Owen provides a reminder of the geology, with Cornbrash limestone visible as large fragments in the field to the west and the Ouse floodplain a step away to the east.

The occurrence of the many irregular limestone cobbles and stones in the fields does not discourage wheat production on these lands, and farmers have learnt how to manage these 'clunch' soils, as they are known, which contain abundant stony rubble. These soils are fertile, despite the potential damage caused to machinery by the stones, and are famous for growing good crops of wheat and barley. A feature of the Ouse was the number of corn mills near it, such as that at Bromham: this fine example has been restored.

Further north, there are a number of small streams draining the north Bedfordshire uplands to the north-west. These small streams, include the Til and Kym, which eventually drain north-east to Grafham Water. Although gently flowing across a flattish landscape, they have cut through the glacial clays and exposed the Oxford Clay and, more rarely, the underlying Oolitic limestone.

Flit Vale

Flit Vale or Flitwick Moor is a small but interesting example of a wet woodland area which is important in the landscape of the county. It is described as a *valley mire* and as such is protected as a Site of Special Scientific Interest (SSSI). What gives this area its distinctive character is the inflow of acid water from the springs of the Lower Greensand. This wetland has led, over time, to the build-up of peat around Flitwick Moor, which was very important in the economy of the district, and peat extraction continued until the 1960s. There is some peat still to be found, which often causes problems for road engineers, as is illustrated by the bypass from Ampthill to Clophill. where there are noticeable undulations caused by the unstable substratum in the peat. Another example of this type of lowland with mixed woodland and rough grazing is at Fancott Woods and Meadows, along the upper stretch of the river and Folly Wood near Flitton. The conservation objective is to improve habitat quality along the course of the Flit River, which has in the past often overtopped its banks creating water meadows. The flooding is now much less common, which is fortunate for the developments encroaching on the floodplain, such as the southern site of Redborne Upper School, Ampthill.

In other places sand and gravel extraction have left old workings, as around Clophill. The most interesting aspect of these areas is the control now exercised by weirs, the straightening of waterways and the deepening of the channels. Dams to provide a reserve for the irrigation of crops, often on the nearby sandy soils, have reduced the flooding risk.

Soils in valley locations are often described as *mosaic*, which is a technical way of describing the mixed and variable nature of soil types over a short distance. There are often sharp contrasts, such as the proximity of well-drained sand and gravels close to peat. This reflects the life of the river, with sand and gravel being carried when the river was in spate and then dumped in quiet areas when flooding subsides. These lower areas flood periodically and gradually are invaded by vegetation, then become a marsh, and finally valley peat.

Red iron staining of the stream in the Flitwick Moor SSSI

The former peat cuttings at Flitwick Moor are now flooded and are a valued wildlife reserve: nearby Flitton Moor is used as rough grazing for cattle. The importance of these areas in the landscape is now recognised, and in some cases efforts are under way to reintroduce a managed flood regime to encourage wet woodland species. The historic value of this land to the people of Maulden was the right to graze animals and gather fuel both wood and peat. The removal of these rights during the period of enclosures resulted in enclosure riots in 1796 when 200 people prevented a survey of the common land. This situation was considered a serious threat to good order and a cavalry troop was drafted in and stationed to Ampthill to prevent conflict. The importance of this alluvial land is demonstrated in the density of important medieval religious houses which cling to the edge of the valley. The religious houses of Beadlow (Beaulieu) Priory and Chicksands Priory were located on the edge of the valley. The moat at Ruxox Farm, just above the floodplain, enclosed a grange (farm) belonging to Dunstable Priory.

The Flit Mineral Waters: A Health Drink

In 1859 an area of some 20 acres adjoining Flitwick Moor was rented to a man called Henry King Stephens, as a smallholding. King is described in the lease as a 'bird stuffer', but was more likely someone who earned his livelihood from wildfowling, with some taxidermy on the side. The plot contained a spring where water from the underlying Greensand aquifer came to the surface. The enterprising new tenant recognised that these waters were rich in iron and, as there was a rising public interest in heath tonics, he marketed this water as a mineral drink. Somehow he managed to gain an endorsement from the eminent medical publication, The Lancet. *Following his death in 1898, the right to bottle the water passed to the R. W. White mineral water company and the waters continued to be marketed until the 1950s. The health benefits depend on the iron content, and this spring is one of many known as 'chalybeate' (rich in iron). The springs at Tunbridge Wells in Kent and Sadler's Wells in London are the best known of these chalybeate waters. Springs emerging from the Greensand are often stained red from iron minerals, and are acid.*

Places to Visit

The Two Moors Heritage Trail at Flitwick (OS Explorer 193) provides an excellent introduction to this landscape. This five-mile route joins the SSSI at Flitwick Moor to the equally important site at Flitton Moor which was managed as rough grazing by both Flitton and Maulden parishes until the enclosures. The approach to Flitton across the moor, with the historic tower of the church built from Greensand as a prominent feature, is especially rewarding. The Heritage Trail can be joined at Flitwick Mill or at Flitton Village. There is good signage maintained by Bedfordshire County Council at Flitton and by the Bedfordshire, Hertfordshire and Buckinghamshire Wildlife Trust at Flitwick Moor. One point to note is the presence of a shooting club, which often makes a Sunday morning walk a noisy experience.

Close to Beadlow, and just east of Clophill, the new 93-hectare Sandy Smith Nature Reserve, owned by the Greensand Trust, is being created from former agricultural and wooded land. The wet woodland is being rejuvenated by careful management of the alder woods, with reed beds and some rough grazing. Clophill Motte (also known as Cainhoe Castle) commands an important crossing-point of the river where it cuts into the Greensand, and a walk to the motte also provides a glimpse of the old gravel and Fuller's Earth extraction pits, which are now flooded and attractive to wintering wildfowl. There is a local nature reserve at Duck End, south of Maulden village, which has been created from old gravel pits.

The Flit Valley as seen from the top of Clophill Motte

CHAPTER 8

THE LANDSCAPE BENEATH OUR FEET

Throughout this book, two themes have been emphasised. First, that the landscape as we see it today owes much to the past and, with a little knowledge, traces of these former landscapes can still be seen in the present-day countryside. Therefore the modern appearance of Bedfordshire, like all of England, owes much to the geological past, including the obvious legacy of mineral extraction, and perhaps less intrusively the way in which the land has been farmed. Second, the landscape is changing all the time: this is a dynamic process which we can see in a human lifespan.

The cultivation of squash in north Bedfordshire

Modern changes in countryside management, for example, have arrested the previous damaging rush to remove hedgerows, and modern tree planting and other environmental inducements are changing the way modern agriculture operates.

Landscape historians have described the English countryside as being like a *palimpsest*, a term used to describe a manuscript or ancient document where earlier writing can be discerned beneath a newer script. The reuse of precious parchment gave an indication of the value of the material before paper became available and affordable.

A more approachable explanation is that the various layers that make up the modern landscape can be peeled away like an onion skin. For example, adjacent to modern tree planting around the Millennium Forest in Marston can be seen ancient woodland, with clear traces of management for coppicing, the plough marks from medieval open-field ploughing, and then more recent brick spoil heaps.

Useful historical benchmarks are hedgerows planted with familiar species such as hawthorn and standards such as ash and elm trees marking off rectangular fields. Many of these hedges are a legacy of the dramatic changes which took place across lowland England when open fields were enclosed in the eighteenth and nineteenth centuries. A survey throughout England over the period 1945 to 1976, using aerial photography, showed a 25 per cent reduction in hedges and this was reinforced by a disastrous reduction of hedge-line trees due to Dutch elm disease in the 1970s.

This removal of boundary hedges was driven by the use of larger machinery and the amalgamation of farm units. More recently, people have begun to understand that the countryside has environmental and recreational value as well as being important for farming. In response, during the 1990s, farmers in England planted around 87 million trees, so beginning a long-term reversal of the national decline in woodland. These are new woodlands and as yet lack the biodiversity of an older wood or hedge.

The complex planning system throughout England now means that all major developments are closely monitored and organisations can be readily mobilised to allow alternative voices to be heard. This can often result in a babble of opinions, usually contradictory. However, a positive outcome is that fundamental changes in land use are scrutinised carefully and there is an opportunity for decisions to be reversed.

Historically, change was far-reaching and had dramatic impact: the enclosures of the common land which took place in the eighteenth and early nineteenth centuries and which did much to shape the modern landscape would be hotly contested at a planning enquiry today, as would the draining of wetlands, or the conversion of heath land to forestry.

One approach to an understanding of the modern countryside is to look at the individual forces which have shaped it throughout time. We have already pieced together the basic structure – the skeleton of the landscape – by looking at the geology, followed by the influence of the last episodes of glaciation. The resulting deposits – so-called *drift*s (as they were once thought to be left behind by icebergs, which dumped much of the superficial material on top of the parent rocks) – largely shaped the agricultural soils, the extraction of sands and gravels, and the topography of Bedfordshire. There is also the impact of climate, which contributes to the colder and wetter clays in the north of the county, and more benign microclimates which favoured market gardening along the major valleys.

Finally, and very importantly, there is man's impact on shaping the landscape. It is this historical record which we tend to see preserved most vividly today, in the field patterns, the landscaped parks and the quarries and extraction pits. In more recent times, countryside change has been viewed in a negative way, when, for example, a new road or a modern wind farm disturbs a favourite view, or a stand of trees is clear-felled.

Many of the factors that shape the landscape also leave a distinct record in the soil, and a study of the distribution and character of the soils in the landscape is helpful in unlocking some of its historical secrets. This chapter provides an outline description of the main soil types in the county and how they play an important part in shaping the landscape beneath our feet.

Mapping Soils in Bedfordshire

England is often described as a nation of gardeners and many people have an intuitive feeling about the land, which is based on gardening and exposure to the countryside. For example, the oft-used garden term *loam* is widely understood as an optimum mix of sand, silt and clay ideal for cropping: it comes as no surprise, then, that much of the Biggleswade market garden tract has loam soils. Additionally, these soils are on gentle slopes, often south-facing, with access to water from the major rivers and the presence of good transport links to the capital. These factors made this an attractive area for the cultivation of a wide range of crops. At the other extreme, the shallow chalk soils, often on steep slopes, in the south of the county were less attractive to agriculture and were ideal for sheep grazing in the past. Sheep are now used to manage conservation areas judged to be too difficult for agricultural use.

This understanding of how soils are important to the economy of an area has a long history. In the closing years of the seventeenth century William

Camden compiled an account of England, county by county. In the 1601 edition, he comments on southern Bedfordshire as having a 'leaner soile but not altogether infertile'. The presence of both the Greensand light sandy soils and the thin soils over the chalk would explain this comment. Much later, the county's enclosure records commonly contain references to soil conditions; for example, in Leighton Buzzard, where a farmer notes that 'the piece of land allotted to me is not worth half the rent'; again a reference to sands over the Greensand Ridge.

By the end of the eighteenth century, systematic surveys of agriculture across the English counties was under way. Arthur Young was appointed to the Board of Agriculture and in 1793, 'arranged for an account of the state of Agriculture in each County'. These accounts were prepared by local residents and in 1794, Thomas Stone published, *A General View of Agriculture in Bedfordshire with Observations on the Means of Improvement.* This was followed in 1808 by a second survey by Thomas Batchelor entitled, A *General View of the Agriculture of the County of Bedford.*

Thomas Batchelor was an interesting personality: he was a poet, a farmer working a Duke of Bedford farm at Lidlington, and also an inventor and improver of agricultural implements. Remarkably, he also became an expert in linguistics and invented a form of shorthand. His account includes a hand-coloured engraved folding frontispiece map with his report reproduced on page 42, which is the first pictorial representation of the soils of the county. This handsome map in three pastel colours demarcates the southern chalk, the Greensand Ridge soils and, finally, in light blues the clays which dominate the county. It is of interest that the major parks of the county are represented on the map; for example, Ampthill, Woburn and Wrest Parks in the centre of the county and Luton Hoo in the south, with a few minor parks in the north.

There is, then, a long gap in the record until the First World War, when the importance of producing food was realised. In 1916, Theodore Rigg of St John's College, Cambridge, surveyed 100 square miles around Biggleswade. '*The soils and crops of the market garden district of Biggleswade*' is a very detailed record using the new ideas from the USA as set out in the US Bureau of Soils. These define areas which could be mapped as relatively uniform tracts of similar soil type, known as a soil series. This detailed description of the soils is accompanied by several maps. This account recognised all of the major soil types in the survey area, and Rigg describes these using the geological foundations as the parent material for the agricultural soils: for example, on Greensand, he identified a 'dark sand' and a 'brown sand'.

In 1916, Rigg was a pioneer in using geology as a basis for soil classification. This was later adopted formally by the government-funded Soil Survey of England and Wales which was responsible for the King survey in 1969. The first systematic scientific national survey of British soils began in the 1950s and its aspiration was to complete the country at a scale of one inch to one mile. Thus, in 1969, *Soils of the Luton and Bedford District A Reconnaissance Survey*, was completed by D. W. King (Special Survey No. 1). This covers all of OS Sheet 147 (one inch to one mile series). This map and the accompanying 39-page record is still the most detailed description of the soils of Bedfordshire and has been used extensively in writing this book.

Some 40 soil series are recognised based on an understanding of the underlying geology – what soil scientists now refer to as the soil parent material. This systematic approach is important, as this is the foundation for the Agricultural Land Classification (ALC) produced in 1969 for the same OS sheet. This was then a five-class system, with the best land in England and Wales being recognised as Class 1, and the land with the most severe problems being classed as Grade 5. This system, with some modification, is still in use today and is often quoted at planning enquiries. Within the five-class system Bedfordshire is significant as having mapped extensive tracts of Class 1 land, mostly in the Ouse and Ivel Valleys and used for horticulture, with some additional patches of Grade 1 on the gentle slopes of the Greensand, where there is sufficient clay to produce loams in areas such as Potton and Clophill.

This county-wide survey was followed in 1987 by a detailed Soil Survey Record (No. 12) of the Biggleswade area, accompanied by a map at a scale of 1:25,000. This survey, carried out by P. S. Wright, covers the entire OS map sheet at the same scale (TL14), and was commissioned to gain additional insights into the important horticultural area bounded by Langford and Sandy, and including villages such as Broom and Caldecote, which are dominated by horticulture. This relatively small area of 100 square kilometres is remarkable for the complexity and variety of soil types recognised. In all, 31 distinct soils were mapped, including deep peat, a soil more characteristic of the Fens, which in turn is adjacent to deep sand deposits. Fertile and easily worked market garden soils with valued loam textures are close to more difficult soils on the Oxford Clays.

Finally, in the 1980s, the Soil Survey of England and Wales, then based at Rothamsted Experimental Station, completed a comprehensive national soil map at a scale of 1:250,000 which described the soil distribution and related land quality across the whole of England and Wales. *Soils and their Use in*

Eastern England includes Bedfordshire and is accompanied by a vividly coloured map sheet. Many of the soil classification names in the county have been changed from the previous reconnaissance survey carried out by King in the 1960s, and correlation of these two maps is a scientific challenge. The organisation responsible for this mapping no longer exists, but all the records are held at Cranfield University and are available at www.landis.org.uk.

Soils in the Landscape

As is stressed throughout this book, the nature of the soil influences much of what we see today in the countryside. Below is a brief outline of the more characteristic soil types found in Bedfordshire. This is not intended to be a full description, nor is it presented using scientific terminology. Rather, it illustrates the variety of soils which occur and which have challenged farmers and growers throughout history. Today these soils remain the basis for agriculture, which is still the most important industry in the county. As explained earlier, an understanding of the landscape flows from an appreciation of the soils and how they have been used throughout history. This approach is best illustrated in the recent publication by Timothy Farewell, Peter Friend, Martin Whiteley and Joanna Zawadzka. Entitled *The Mapping of Landscapes, Geology, and Soils in Bedfordshire and Cambridgeshire*, and published by the Bedfordshire Geology Group in 2011, this brief document provides a useful guide to the structure of the county.

The Chalk

Beginning in the south of the county there is a suite of soils associated with the chalk geology: these are most distinctive. On the chalk plateau, as the land slopes south towards Hertfordshire a winter walk will result in heavy boots with a clod of sticky clay clinging stubbornly to each foot. This is the result of what is commonly described as 'clay with flints', the hard flint nodules being frequent in every ploughed field. The exact history and origin of this clay with flints (or *plateau drift* deposit) has been the subject of lots of scientific research especially as the world-famous Rothamsted Research Station, across the border in Hertfordshire, is sited on this soil type. What is clear is that this deposit is related to glaciation. The strong winds which accompanied the glacial period moved silt-sized particles of soil onto the plateau, and these are now mixed with more clay-rich weathered material from the underlying chalk.

All of these deposits are old and have had much of the residual calcium from the chalk removed by rain water over time. In a few localities there are isolated deposits of pure wind-deposited material known as *brickearths*, as they yielded in small quantities a useful brick- making clay; an example is at Gaddesden Row and at Caddington close to the Hertfordshire border. The latter has yielded many Palaeolithic tools made from local flint, which illustrates that occupation of these uplands was under way not long after the ice retreated from southern England. Cultivation of all of these soils requires skill as they can be damaged by the use of heavy machines when wet. There is also appreciable wear on farm implements by the flint stones.

The most recognisable chalk landscape is of course the Downs, and soils here are shallow and lie directly over the bedrock. These soils are common to other areas in the Chilterns and in agricultural terms their shallowness and lack of adequate rooting depth, plus the steepness of the slopes, make these locations useful only for grazing. There are, however, relic signs of ancient cultivation terraces where Iron Age farmers have thrown up retaining banks to capture soil washing downslope and enclose small fields. The present-day land use is either for sheep or for open-access land, much valued for walking and kite flying and often providing a rich botanical mixture of chalk-loving plants. One problem with these soils is that they are fragile, so that much-used footpaths will break through the grass cover and encourage water erosion, resulting in ugly scars on the hillside. Technically, these soils are referred to as *rendzinas*.

The Greensand

The Greensand Ridge which traverses Bedfordshire is enjoyed by walkers for the variety of landscapes, fine views across the lower clay vales, and for easy walking across normally dry and sandy soils. This is not always the case, however, as in many places there is a thin clay cap left by the glacial ice which results in a more sticky clay soil. However, where the Greensand is close to the surface good walking is the result, with Rushmere and Ampthill Parks being fine examples. In a few places the sandy soils have been so leached of all nutrients and colour just below the root zone that a distinct ash-grey layer is clearly seen, as in the illustration overleaf from Apsley Heath.

Where the soils are covered by a thin layer of clay or have benefited from the washing-in of clay from above, these become agriculturally useful, combining good drainage and a fertile topsoil from the clay. Around Potton, for example, there is Class 2 agricultural land. At one time the Rothamsted Experimental Station operated an outstation at Woburn to gain experience in the cultivation of these soils.

Podzol soil profile at Apsley Heath (Shirrel Heath series)

However, in general within this upland sandy belt, land has never been heavily farmed and today Greensand areas are used for recreation, such as golf, forestry and parkland. The Duke of Bedford proved in the late eighteenth century that coniferous woodland could be grown on these soils, and plantation woods are still a significant land use and feature of this landscape.

Soils of the Clay Vales

Puddled soils damaged by horses grazing on the Oxford Clays

The Greensand Ridge divides the two distinctive clay vales which cross the county, both of which are now important agricultural areas. Only the presence of well-maintained under-field drainage makes these soils useful and historically these would have been wasteland. The Marston Clays are typical of this area, and north of Wilstead is an area formerly known as the 'Bedfordshire Fens', before it was successfully drained. These clays are what John Bunyan would have struggled to cross when he described the 'slough of despond', as he approached the Ampthill area from Bedford. The soils are described as slowly permeable, clayey, and seasonally waterlogged: in any language, wet. The excavations for the realigned A421 from Brogborough to Bedford cross these clays and the uniform grey of the subsoil is evidence of the seasonally wet conditions. In February 2014 this road was closed due to flooding at Marston.

Similarly, the Gault Clays around Barton and eastwards to Wimpole are described as 'a stiff grey calcareous clay'. Farming this soil requires local knowledge and a careful watch on the weather, especially in spring. The soils are usually unworkable from November to March and therefore farmers need to take a weather break in the early autumn to allow cultivation. The modern techniques of direct drilling and minimum cultivation with only periodic ploughing and subsoiling when conditions are optimum can now be used effectively to manage the soils and produce good crops of winter cereals, with autumn-sown oilseed rape also common. This is not a livestock area, due to winter rain, and the photo above of land used by horses near Marston illustrates the problem, with areas around gates, for example, prone to damage in wet conditions. Additionally, the impact of fluoride from the brick-making process on the health of cattle discouraged the livestock industry.

Brick-making and a Whiff of Sulphur

During the 1970s the brick-making industry in the Marston Vale faced the realisation that the existing plant was aging, and investment in larger and more modern equipment was essential. Plans were developed to construct a 'superworks' facility and submitted to the planning authorities. To the surprise of the London Brick Company, the plans initiated a public campaign to oppose the plant and a Public Review of Brickmaking and the Environment (PROBE) began to question the environmental standards to be adopted. Attention focused on the emissions from the firing of brick, which results in a combination of gases, including compounds of sulphur and fluorides. The distinctive smell of the brick-making plants was due to mercaptans, which are compounds containing sulphur and carbon from the brick clays combined with hydrogen. The debate centred on the impact on public health and the impact of fluorosis in cattle. The opponents of the expanded plant argued that a wasting disease in cattle, resulting from grazing on land downwind of the Marston plants, would impact on animal production. The company argued that the technology required to clean the emissions would make the works uneconomic. In the late 1970s the problem disappeared as an economic downturn reduced the demand for bricks and new investment in the Marston plants became unlikely. In 1981, the Ridgmont plant closed, with the loss of 1,100 jobs.

The Clay Uplands

As mentioned in Chapter 8, Bedfordshire is dominated by clay soils. In the centre and north of the county a mantle of glacial boulder clay or drift is only interrupted by the major river valleys. In contrast to the clay vales described above, the presence of low hills and sloping land assists in carrying rainfall away, and helps reduce any standing water. Despite these difficulties, this belt provides some of the most extensive cereal-growing land in England. The presence of calcium from the underlying chalky boulder clay strengthens the structure of the soils and this helps the internal drainage of the land. Nevertheless, field drains are essential in these wet soils and allow farmers to work on the land, especially in autumn. The influence of climate is also a feature in this belt, with the average number of days when it would be damaging to work with machinery on the land being around 90 per year in the drier east and centre of Bedfordshire, and closer to 150 days per year in the north-west close to the Northamptonshire border. Where the soils are drier there are opportunities for spring cultivations and more variety in cropping, with beans and potatoes being grown.

The Soils of the River Valleys

Rough grazing close to the River Flit

The Ouse and Ivel Valleys and the adjacent river terraces are the jewel in the crown of Bedfordshire agricultural land, with the Biggleswade horticultural industry based on these productive, deep and well-drained soils, which occur on gentle slopes and close to water supplies available for irrigation. In contrast, the Flit Valley has residual peat, and the Ouse Valley has good examples of flood meadows used for rough grazing. In other areas, stands of alders and willow provide the necessary cover for wildlife; the county has seen a remarkable return of the otter over the past decade.

The sense of building modern housing, retail parks and other infrastructure on these soils and on floodplains has recently been called into question, with the increased risk and incidence of flooding. While these buildings can be protected by engineering works, this simply decreases the overflow capacity of rivers in times of flood and increases the likelihood of simply moving problems downstream.

The Horticultural Soils of the Ouse and Ivel Valleys

Market gardening grew to become a major industry based on these favourable soil conditions, and the success of the cropping depended mainly on the thickness of the loamy soil deposits over the underlying gravels. The presence of the last glaciation can still be seen on these soils from careful inspection of aerial photographs which reveal patterned ground which is a relic of Arctic permafrost conditions, causing variable depths of soil over the gravel sub-strata: this can cause differential growth in crops, especially in dry years. The soils are well drained on level or gently sloping river terraces, with an abundance of stones in the topsoil. Winter rain is quickly absorbed.

Along the Ouse and Ivel Valleys the long-established practice of using irrigation from groundwater has lowered the regional water table, allowing these soils to be worked for long periods. The importance of this area and its soils has long been recognised. In the county reports, Batchelor (1808) notes that 'the subsoil of gravel is covered with a great thickness of black mould or red-brown earth and in both of them the fertility is very great; every sort of corn, or seeds, never failing to yield an ample crop.'

The importance of adding organic material to these soils has been understood by growers for some time, and the practice of adding manure from London was common and greatly expanded with the arrival of the railways. On light, well-drained soils the addition of any organic materials is beneficial – which is why modern gardeners use compost to increase the soil's organic content. A further source of organic material was shoddy, which was a by-product of the textile industry. The shoddy waste was the scraps of wool and yarn left over in the manufacture of wool textiles. Adding this to soils in the area was still common in the 1970s.

A botanical curiosity of this use of wool shoddy was the introduction of exotic weeds from Australia and South America, which were imported with the wool: some 400 species have been noted. The extent of area under vegetable production was at its maximum during the Second World War, and this coincided with the comprehensive and systematic Land Utilisation Survey of Britain, carried out in 1943. The list of crops grown in this area, as listed below, is astonishing: 'All market garden crops are grown: early and late potatoes, Brussels sprouts, peas, runner beans, carrots, beetroot, parsley, vegetable marrows, parsnips, cauliflowers, cabbage, lettuce, and onions. Some flowers are grown. Potatoes and Brussels sprouts are of outstanding importance.'

Flit Vale

The River Flit is a tributary of the Ivel, which in turn joins the Ouse, and this valley is characterised by the presence of deep peat along the river line. Peat was extracted from this area from the seventeenth century until 1960, and much of this land has now reverted to rough grazing. Roman pottery found below the peat during extraction illustrates that this peat infill has taken place over a 2,000-year time span.

The presence of lowland valley mire, as this area is technically described, is uncommon in lowland England, making the area an important nature reserve, with SSSI status. The importance of this reserve is recognised by the many fungi species recorded, including one rare example. Flitwick Moor is one of the few sites in the UK where this specimen is still to be found. The character of the vegetation is changing, however, as the former acid springs which fed into the watercourse dry out as the regional water table is lowered. Inflow is then replaced by alkaline inflow from the River Flit, which has its headwaters on the chalk. When the river is high, the more base-rich waters of the river spill into the mire and influence the acid plant life, which is usually nurtured by the iron-rich, more acid springs from the Greensand rocks: these iron-rich springs were at one time bottled and sold as health tonics. Elsewhere along the valley, there are stretches of wet alluvial soils which are variable in character, and which flood periodically.

CHAPTER 9

PEOPLE AND THE LANDSCAPE

If this chapter had been written 20 years ago with the same title, the 'people' referred to in the title would have been mostly farmers, with a few foresters, and perhaps a gamekeeper or two. Now the shift in public understanding of the countryside and the pressure for more varied use of the land has meant that interest in the countryside has expanded to ramblers, bird watchers, anglers, mountain-bike enthusiasts, horse riders, county-sports groups, archaeologists and those with metal detectors, and a host of specialist organisations concerned with nature conservation.

The long-distance Greensand Ridge footpath crossing Ampthill Great Park

Strict planning laws have meant that local government at all levels is charged with an array of responsibilities, from the maintenance of footpaths to tree preservation orders. There is also a large and often confusing number of protection schemes to encourage conservation, access to land and recreation in the countryside.

This chapter works on the premise that anyone who has read this far is interested enough to want to understand more, or may already be involved in some way in activities that encourage access to the countryside. It would be impossible to list here the work of the many organisations involved in countryside management. Nor is it appropriate to attempt to explain the many ways in which the countryside is protected through legislation: indeed, this would require detailed knowledge of the planning system. Therefore all this chapter can hope to achieve is to act as a signpost for those interested to research further.

It is important to realise that responsibility for the appearance of the landscape in England today rests mostly with thousands of farm businesses, both big and small, which make decisions each year based on prices, costs, the labour available, the weather over the last few seasons, and which crops or products government agencies and the international market are encouraging through incentive schemes. Decisions reflect an intimate knowledge of the land they farm. Most of the decisions made about the countryside are therefore in private hands, and it is only necessary to apply for planning permission for major changes in land use. However, embedded within this landscape are hundreds of small, and some larger, areas which are designated in some way and therefore have stricter planning controls or may be in public ownership.

Bedfordshire is blessed with an array of these sites and each has a special, often unique, character which is of interest in some way, and has brought the location into a special category of protection. Described below is a listing – not claimed to be comprehensive – of the areas in Bedfordshire that receive some form of protection. Many of these are well-known, such as the Chilterns Area of Outstanding Natural Beauty (AONB); many more are modest and listed simply as County Wildlife Sites (CWSs) or bird reserves, and are known only to a few specialists. This is followed by a very brief introduction to some of the many organisations which are active in conservation and access issues in the county.

Designated Protected Areas in Bedfordshire: Chilterns AONB

The characteristic steep scarp slope of the chalk, at its best in Bedfordshire with Dunstable Downs and other outstanding chalk slopes between Luton and Hitchin, qualify this area as worthy of special protection, which takes the form of designation as an Area of Outstanding Natural Beauty (AONB). Across England, 35 sites have achieved this status. The Chilterns AONB reaches into the county from the west where it stretches to the Thames Gap at Goring. The definition of an AONB is that it must have significant landscape value. However, ownership of the land remains largely with private individuals, and conservation relies on planning controls, along with sensitive countryside management. These areas represent the best of the chalk landscape. It is estimated that, along its length, the Chilterns are within easy reach of some nine million people, which means this is an important recreation area for a large part of the population of south-east England. Access to the attractive area is best along the Ridgeway, a National Trail running eastwards from Oxfordshire, which terminates at Ivinghoe Beacon, where the Ridgeway joins with the Icknield Way. This path then carries on east to join Peddars Way, linking the trail into Norfolk. Within this AONB are many other smaller protected sites and nature reserves which carry other landscape designations, such as the Barton Hills National Nature Reserve.

National Nature Reserves (NNRs)

There are 222 NNRs in England, representing many of the finest wildlife and geological sites in the country. The first NNRs emerged in the post-war years alongside the early National Parks, and numbers have continued to grow since then. NNRs were initially established to protect sensitive features and to provide outdoor laboratories for natural science research. Their purpose has widened since those early days. As well as managing some of the country's most valued habitats, our rarest species and our most significant geology, most reserves now offer great opportunities to the public as well as schools and specialist audiences to experience England's natural heritage. In Bedfordshire only three areas have been listed as NNRs: the Barton Hills and Knocking Hoe on the chalk escarpment (both of which are also within the AONB described above) and Kings Wood, on the nearby Greensand Ridge, close to Heath and Reach, and adjacent to Rushmere Country Park.

The Barton Hills NNR is important due to the presence of rare plants suited to chalk soils, together with a butterfly population including the rare Chalkhill Blue. Much of the scarp slope has been disturbed in the past by quarrying for lime. The land was grazed by a flock of Dorset Horn sheep in the early twentieth century, but when this grazing was stopped there was extensive scrub encroachment, especially hawthorn and coarse grasses. Grazing by rabbits was also reduced following the *myxomatosis* outbreak in the 1950s. At present controlled grazing is allowed and the scrub removed where possible. The Knocking Hoe site is in a similar location, with a similar ecology; the main difference is that this site is on private land.

The interest in Kings Wood is due to soils derived from the Greensand which are characteristically sandy and support bracken, heather and birch trees. However, there is also a cap of glacial boulder clay, which leads to oak and other broad-leaved species on the less sandy land. This should not be confused with another King's Wood, also on the Greensand Ridge and designated as an SSSI, which is close to Ampthill. Both woods are the now-reduced relics of formerly more extensive hunting reserves.

Forestry Commission Land

The land owned and managed by the Forestry Commission in the county is referred to as Ampthill Forest, which leads to some confusion since, locally, the main site is known as Maulden Wood. In fact, the designation, Ampthill Forest, covers three additional locations: at Wilstead, Potton and Stanford. As with Kings Wood, (the NNR at Heath and Reach, described above), Maulden Wood is an attractive mix of broad-leaved woodland and acidic grassland, as it straddles both the sandstones and the clay cap deposited by glaciation. This site also remarkably includes two SSSIs: the acidic grassland in the centre of the site is of ecological interest, and the northern part of the site is a large remnant of ancient woodland on the glacial boulder clay.

Wilstead Wood is also an ancient woodland site which is being restored, removing the more recent conifers. This wood is one of a handful of ancient woodlands within the Marston Vale Community Forest. Potton Wood is another ancient woodland site and has been managed by coppicing in the past.

The Forest of Marston Vale

In 1994 the government launched 12 Community Forests throughout England. A 158 square kilometre tract of county between Bedford and Milton Keynes which had been adversely affected by decades of clay extraction for brick-making from the Oxford Clay Vale was selected for Community Forest status. The challenge was to use trees and woodlands to repair the scarred landscape and at the same time revitalise the communities around the forest. The target is to plant six million trees by 2031; as of mid-2008, one million had been planted. Within the forest area is the 225-hectare Millennium Country Park, a focal point of which is the Forest Centre building, which opened in 2000 and is now used for a variety of community and business gatherings. The presence of this national forest will introduce a wooded landscape along the improved A421 road corridor south of Bedford.

Community Forests: More Than Just Trees

The idea of Community Forests was inspired by forward-thinking planners in Europe. In the Netherlands, an ambitious forestation scheme was begun in 1934, to provide employment during economic depression, in an area close to Amsterdam. The aim was to provide recreational space for the growing city, which was linked to the new woodland by an electric tram. Today the Amsterdam Bos provides access to a range of recreational opportunities and contains mature woodland, parkland, riverside trails and, of course, cycleways. The recreational nature of these forests was pioneered by the provision of sports pitches, bridleways and even a dry ski slope. In England the Community Forests are now well-established recreational locations, as is evident at Marston Vale.

The Woodland Trust

Founded in 1972, the Woodland Trust is the largest of the woodland conservation bodies active in the UK, and relies mostly on private donations. In Bedfordshire there are a number of sites owned and managed by this organisation, including a large block of ancient woodland at Reynolds Wood close to Brogborough. The overall Woodland Trust site includes the existing Hulcote Wood as well as new planting. This site is close to 100 hectares in size and is part of the Marston Vale Forest. At the other end of the scale are a small number of pocket-sized woods such as at Gullivers Spinney at Souldrop, which is a mere 2 hectares.

Country Parks

The Millennium Country Park mentioned above is one of the five country parks located within the county, which provide recreational access to a range of landscapes typical of Bedfordshire. The country park concept is deliberately designed to provide recreation space in a rural setting within easy reach of growing urban populations. They therefore differ from the many other designated areas in that they are primarily for recreational use and do not view landscape conservation as a priority, nor do they represent any unique ecology. Bedfordshire, with an ever-expanding area of land being built on, is considered deficient in terms of natural or semi-natural green space, and the country parks are an attempt to redress this. Many sites make use of former mineral extraction areas and so transform what was viewed as derelict land into useful and well-used land. For example, the Millennium Park close to the village of Marston has a backdrop of the surviving brick kiln chimneys as a constant reminder of the industry that thrived here for many decades. The clay pits are now flooded and provide winter refuges for wildfowl and a facility for water sports.

Priory Country Park within the urban area of Bedford provides a welcome space for recreation for townspeople and is also centred on now-flooded mineral extraction workings, this time in the old gravel workings along the Ouse Valley. The site, on the edge of land once held by Newham Priory, has been transformed and is now an important area for sailing, cycling, bird watching and walking.

Rushmere Country Park, in contrast, is located on the Greensand Ridge and includes one of the Sites of Special Scientific Interest (SSSI) in the county. The landscape here is typical of the broken countryside of the Ridge, with occasional steep dry valleys and a vegetation of bracken, heather and birch.

Harrold-Odell Country Park in north Bedfordshire, like Priory Country Park, is typical of older gravel working sites along the Ouse Valley which have been sensitively reclaimed. Close by Odell Great Wood is one the best examples of ancient woodland in the county, dominated by oak with hazel coppice and accessible from the country park.

Finally, on the chalk landscapes to the south of the county is the Sundon Hills Country Park. Set in the Chilterns AONB, near the village of Sundon, this 93-acre country park offers views of the surrounding countryside, especially the clay vales to the north. There are waymarked walks taking in woods, chalk hillsides and grassland.

Sites of Special Scientific Interest (SSSIs)

Areas designated as SSSIs represent the most important wildlife and geological sites in the UK. They include the most special and beautiful habitats, which are considered a priority for conservation and part of the national heritage. These unique and varied habitats have developed over hundreds of years through careful management practices such as grazing or forestry. In Bedfordshire, 40 sites have been set aside as SSSIs, and these include the area of Barton Hills, described above as an NNR; this area is also included within the Chilterns AONB, which illustrates the overlapping way in which these conservation designations work. The Barton SSSI area is only some 50 hectares, within a chalk valley or *coombe*, and includes unimproved grassland on the chalk with many species of wild flowers and grasses and also a small beech wood and a spring issuing from the chalk.

Many of these 40 sites within Bedfordshire are small and not obviously very visually attractive. An example is the small compact wetland at Dropshort, just south of Toddington, which represents a type of wetland habitat once common in southern England where a series of springs issue at the junction of glacial gravels with the underlying impervious Oxford Clay. The marsh has interesting vegetation, rich in both marsh and meadow species. An unusual feature of the marsh is a small area of 'quaking bog'. The type of habitat, although previously widely distributed in lowland Britain, has been greatly reduced both in extent and quality as a result of drainage and changes in agricultural practice.

Other SSSI sites in the county are very well known, such as the lowland heath of Cooper's Hill adjacent to Ampthill Park and the ancient wood at Marston Thrift, now within the Marston Vale Forest.

Local Nature Reserves (LNRs)

All local authorities have the power to acquire, declare and manage these sites, and in Bedfordshire 20 areas are classified as LNRs. The site must have a value locally for wildlife, geology, education or simply public enjoyment. The local authority (LA) can lease or own the site, or manage the site with the agreement of the owner. This designation as an LNR category falls between statutory sites of national importance such as NNRs, and the more numerous and local County Wildlife Sites described below. In some cases in the county an LNR is also recognised as an SSSI, such as at Cooper's Hill or the Galley and Warden Hill. The Harrold-Odell Country Park is also recognised as an LNR. In many cases the management of the site is handed over to a local group of volunteers, such as at the Stotfold Watermill Nature Reserve, which is managed by a group called TEASEL, centring on Astwick and Stotfold. Brown's Wood on the outskirts of Clapham is another notable LNR with some 6 hectares of ancient woodland which was supplemented by new woodland planting of 10 hectares at the millennium.

County Wildlife Sites (CWSs)

These are common in the county, with more than 500 being identified. Most are small fragments but important locally. They have no statuary protection and are identified by a panel of ecologists and conservation officers as being significant for wildlife and contributing to the richness and diversity of the countryside. These sites are regularly monitored for change by the Bedfordshire Biodiversity Recording and Monitoring Centre. Overall, CWSs account for some 7 per cent of the area of Bedfordshire. There is often no public access to the land apart from existing rights of way, and control over management remains with the landowner. However, the recognition of a CWS will help to attract grant aid finance and other environmental stewardship assistance. A typical site is the Blunham disused railway site, which is accessible from the Route 51 cycleway along the Ouse Valley, or King's Wood close to Houghton Conquest, which is famous for spring bluebells or, surprisingly, the churchyard at St Andrews, the parish church of Ampthill.

Regionally Important Geological and Geomorphological Sites (RIGS)

These are sites with a special importance to geologists and are the equivalent of the CWSs mentioned above: 21 of these are identified in Bedfordshire. In addition, there are six sites that are important to geologists which are already within the SSSIs, as described above. Therefore the well-known Totternhoe Stone Quarry is an SSSI and also a RIGS. Excellent examples of this local designation are the abandoned sand quarries around Leighton Buzzard, such as at Ledburn and Tiddenfoot (where the adjacent quarry has been transformed into Tiddenfoot Waterside Park). These are classic geological sites where the Woburn Sands strata are represented by very pure sand which was laid down in an ancient seaway. A close examination of the face of the quarry wall shows a cross-section through sands laid down as on a beach, with ripple marks made by ancient currents. It is important to recognise the hazards of entering any quarry: the dangers of land slippage, deep water and trespass must be understood.

Signage for a new woodland planted as part of the Marston Vale

Wildlife Trust Sites in Bedfordshire

Bedfordshire is linked to Cambridgeshire and Northamptonshire in one large Wildlife Trust organisation which manages 119 nature reserves. Some sites, such as the heathland at Cooper's Hill, have already been mentioned as SSSIs, but many are small and protected for specific reasons. In Bedfordshire there are 27 sites, which are representative of the diversity of the county. An example is the Pavenham Osier Beds, which at one time supplied a local basket-making industry, and another small but interesting site is located above the village of Barton on the site of an old chalk quarry. Some sites are on reclaimed land, released after quarrying or gravel workings, such as at Cople.

Perhaps the most exciting of the projects being implemented by the Wildlife Trust for Bedfordshire, Cambridgeshire and Northamptonshire are referred to as *Living Landscapes.* Nationally there are 150 of these large-scale initiatives, with only two located in Bedfordshire. The concept is based on the view that often, in conservation, people become the outsiders – looking in at preserved wildlife sites. The Living Landscapes idea involves more communities and businesses and aims to create a resilient countryside, which is more than just fragmented conservation sites. In Bedfordshire, the *Totternhoe Initiative* includes some 200 hectares and is located on the edge of the chalk in the south of the county. The intention is to link two existing SSSIs and at the same time provide educational and recreational facilities for the urban populations of Luton and Dunstable. Second, *the Flit Vale Landscape Initiative* has already added two important conservation sites. Folly Wood, adjacent to the existing SSSI close to Flitwick, enlarges the area of valley mire under protection, and upstream in the Flit Valley the Fancott SSSI, close to Toddington, has both grassland and ancient woodland. The challenge is to link these in some way.

Bird Reserves

The Lodge at Sandy is the national headquarters of the Royal Society for the Protection of Birds (RSPB) in the UK and there is an associated 180-hectare wooded site managed for wildlife, especially birds, surrounding the offices. The area is characteristic of the Greensand Ridge, with woodland, open grassland and the largest stretch of open lowland heath in the county. One feature of this reserve is the complex of Iron Age forts, including Galley Hill.

The National Trust (NT) in Bedfordshire

The NT manages just over 200 hectares of land at the Chiltern Gateway site on Dunstable Downs, which allows access to many of the best walks on the chalk uplands. In addition, close by is the well-known site (4 hectares) of the Whipsnade Tree Cathedral, created after the First World War. Towards the east of the county, just over the border in Cambridgeshire, the Trust also owns and manages the magnificent Wimpole Hall, with an associated landscape park and model farm, a total area of 1,200 hectares. This park was created in the early eighteenth century, simply by removing the existing villages. Much of the land has never been ploughed since, and therefore Wimpole is now an island of preserved landscape surrounded by the more typical Bedfordshire and Cambridgeshire tracts of intensive arable farming. The remains of the great formal gardens are still discernible, as are signs of the ridge and furrow which predated these, and faint traces of the former villages.

English Heritage in Bedfordshire

English Heritage has the broad remit of managing the historic buildings of England, and has the stewardship of a large number of historic sites, including great houses and nationally significant gardens. In the county the best-known example is Wrest Park Gardens, with around 90 hectares of historic landscapes surrounding the house. The formal canals and woodland areas were originally laid out in the seventeenth century by owners influenced by Dutch garden design. In the following century 'Capability' Brown was allowed to 'soften the edges' of the formal gardens, but he was kept in check and not permitted to sweep away the established structure. The gardens are therefore celebrated as having both the formal elements of the early layouts, with wooded walks and canals, and the later, more naturalised landscapes of Brown, with the lake and accompanying canal. When the current mansion was built in the 1830s the Italian garden was added, but designed to complement the much earlier garden structure. The complicated management of the hydrology of the site is important as the gardens, lakes and canals are located mostly on the Gault Clay, which easily retains water, while the house and kitchen garden were on the edge of these clays and have a loamier and more accommodating soil for cultivation. After the Second World War, the site became the headquarters for the National Institute for Agricultural Engineering, and a soil survey in 1945 mapped the soils which were to be used in experimental trials. The fields adjacent to the impressive entrance drive, which were just slightly elevated above the Gault Clay, are therefore valued as free-draining, loam soils, in contrast to the land south and east of the Wrest Park House, where impervious clays provide a challenge to cultivation.

Other sites managed by English Heritage in Bedfordshire include Bushmead Priory, Houghton House and the De Grey Mausoleum at Flitton.

The Sandy Smith Nature Reserve

All of the above sites have some form of public ownership or management. A welcome addition is an entirely private venture east of Clophill where a local landowner has set aside a former arable area of around 90 hectares as a nature reserve and handed this over to the Greensand Trust for management as a nature reserve. This area abuts onto the River Flit, which flows parallel to the A507 at this point, and there is a stand of alder woodland, a reed bed and grazing land on one of the few areas of peat remaining in the valley. Careful management of the river bank will encourage the possibility of otters eventually colonising undisturbed sites such as this. The northern boundary on the boulder clay soils borders the Chicksands Woods and Ministry of Defence (MOD) estate and firing range. Red kites were first spotted here in the summer of 2009, and have been seen regularly since.

Local Parks

Ampthill Great Park is hardly a local park, attracting visitors from well outside the county, but it is local in that it is owned and administered by Ampthill Town Council. The Park is an excellent example of the Greensand Ridge and contains many features which are characteristic of this upland landscape, including a very small outcrop of Greensand, a spring line where the more permeable sandstone meets the impermeable Oxford Clay along the base of the steep north-facing scarp, small dry valleys and relics of an older landscape design created by 'Capability' Brown, with planted groups of pine trees. The long-distance Greensand Ridge footpath runs directly through the Park along the scarp and from this vantage point there are splendid views to the north across the Oxford Clays, the Ouse terraces and beyond to the northern boulder clay hills north of Bedford. The Greensand Trust is active is assisting with the management of the Park, which has survived from a former hunting reserve for royal visitors in the sixteenth century. It is acknowledged that the Park is heavily used and needs careful management, with public consultation at the centre of any initiatives. The reintroduction of grazing cattle in the Park, for example, was carefully explained as a management technique to prevent scrub encroachment.

In contrast, Flitwick Manor Park, along the valley of the River Flit and bounded by the busy A507, is more intimate. This small reserve has a good example of wet woodland and also a preserved park landscape around the former manor house, which is now a hotel. There is, for example, a well-preserved ha-ha, and an interesting collection of exotic mature trees, brought to the UK as seeds from all over the world by an enthusiastic plant collector. The Park is owned and managed by Flitwick Town Council.

Organisations working to protect and allow access to the countryside have blossomed over the last decade, and with funding available from a variety of sources the role of these groups has become ever more important. The abbreviated notes below serve only to illustrate the variety of organisations which are active in the county; the list is not meant to be comprehensive. In many cases, the management of the sites described above has been devolved to these organisations and they are usually very keen to welcome volunteers in many different capacities.

Chilterns Commons Project: Local Management of Common Land

Commons have been at the heart of rural communities since medieval times, but today they are often overlooked or taken for granted. The Chilterns has around 200 areas of common land, ranging from strips of grass verge to rolling hectares of wildflower-rich grassland and woodland, and these play a vital role in the natural and cultural heritage of the Chilterns AONB. Commons are very important wildlife habitats, brilliant natural playgrounds and contain centuries of local history within them. The Chilterns Commons Project is a four-year initiative which was launched in 2011 and coordinated by the Chilterns Conservation Board with a grant of over £400,000 from the Heritage Lottery Fund. This project aims to reconnect people with their common land for walking, playing and enjoying the outdoors. It also aims to inspire and enable people to get involved with actively caring for commons and studying them, in order to build up a historical record of our Chilterns commons and an idea of how they are faring ecologically. Within Bedfordshire there are at least nine areas included, such as Lilley Hoo, Whipsnade Heath and Studham. The 60-hectare site at Studham is interesting as it includes land typical of the 'clay with flints' plateau, with clay soils overlying chalk: the area has been used for common grazing in the past, but was ploughed up during the Second World War. The common has now been restored to general use and is managed by a local group, the Friends of Studham Common. A management plan is in place and visitors are encouraged to visit by a colourful information leaflet, which outlines a short walk. The dormouse, a protected species, has been recorded at the site.

The Greensand Trust

The Trust aims to work with landowners to conserve and promote the distinctive landscape of the Greensand Ridge, by improving access and providing information and independent, technical advice if required. The means by which the Trust operates is to create partnerships with local people and interest groups; with local councils in the region which have responsibilities for conservation and access; with local businesses engaged in environmental work; and – most importantly – with local landowners who are willing to allow public access. The creation of the Greensand Trust recognised that the Ridge and its environment were constantly changing, and that in Bedfordshire there is increasing and constant pressure on green space as housing and other infrastructure development in the south-east of England increases. The danger is that these green spaces will become fragmented and form a less attractive habitat for wildlife. The target is eventually to raise funds to buy land in key environmental areas. Meanwhile, the Trust provides a management and ranger service along the Ridge and is active on numerous sites.

Land Restoration Projects

The impressive transformation of the landscapes within Marston Vale has already been mentioned in the context of the Forest of Marston Vale and the Millennium Country Park. This area was scarred by the brick-making industry centred on the Oxford Clay, and the physical evidence of this industrial landscape is still evident in the impressive chimneys. Less obvious but no less important throughout the county is the extraction of sand and aggregates.

Bedfordshire produces almost 2 million tonnes of sand and gravel each year, including the alluvial sand and gravels of the Ouse and Ivel, and the much older sands of the Greensand Ridge, including specialist deposits such as Fuller's Earth. All of these deposits have long been associated with finding archaeological remains, such as the complicated history of human settlement at Harrold and Odell, which stretches from Neolithic flint implements to Romano-British farms, and then Saxon settlements. There is now a review under way – the *Bedfordshire Aggregates Archaeological Assessment* – for Central Bedfordshire Council to record and map the extent of aggregate production sites in the county, and to audit the present state of knowledge of archaeological resources.

In a similar way the *Sand Pit Project*, supported by the Greensand Trust, is aiming to work with the aggregates industry, especially around Leighton

Buzzard, to increase awareness of the potential of former sites for restoration and conservation. The project has negotiated leases for inactive quarry sites and has worked to restore these as nature reserves and open up permissive paths linking to established rights of way.

The Long-Distance Footpath Network

The dense network of footpaths, bridleways and green lanes, augmented by permissive paths, are a unique and treasured part of the English countryside. Local authorities now dedicate much time, finance and effort to maintaining these. Despite persistent grumbles, the signposting, stiles and footbridges on these paths continue to improve. In addition, the county has a number of long-distance paths, which cross a variety of landscapes and provide an intimate view of the countryside; these are described in more retail in Chapter 10.

The classification of these ambitious routes begins with National Trails, such as the iconic Hadrian's Wall path in Northumberland, but none of these exist in Bedfordshire. The premier walking organisation in the UK, the Ramblers, does not seem to list any long-distance routes in the county; however, the Greensand Ridge Walk (GRW), which runs from Leighton Buzzard in the west to Gamlingay in the east, a distance of some 40 miles, provides along its length views of every type of countryside. The route has been subdivided into five easy sections for day walks and there is a route description for each.

The GRW crosses many of the areas already described in this guide, and takes in country Parks, SSSIs and LNRs as well as linking villages of character. Other important walking routes in the county include the Ridgeway Link, which joins the National Trail of the Ridgeway from Beacon Hill close to Ivinghoe to the Dunstable Downs Gateway Centre. This then allows access to the Icknield Way, eastwards from Dunstable. The intention is that this path eventually achieves National Trail status, which would form part of a network of trails which link the south coast of England and the Wash. For real walkers, the best introduction to Bedfordshire is the Bunyan Way, which loops through the county for 75 miles, beginning and ending at the Sundon Hills Country Park. This route crosses all of the main Bedfordshire landscapes and passes close to many of the places associated with John Bunyan, the Puritan evangelist and author of *Pilgrim's Progress*. If Bedfordshire is a mainly a county of clay, then it is appropriate to complete this section with the 12-mile *Clay Way* walk from Bromham to Ridgmont. This walk follows the boulder clay hills in the west of the county and provides good views of Marston Vale and the Greensand Ridge. The footpath is often muddy – the clue is in the title of the walk.

And on a Bike

The growing enthusiasm for cycling has been recognised in the county and there are routes now waymarked to provide for all interests. At the national level, Route 51, the University Way, links Oxford to Cambridge, passing through Milton Keynes and Bedford, joining the north–south Route 12 close to Sandy. Access to this well-paved route, which is partly on dedicated cycleways and also on minor roads, is easiest from the Marston or Priory County Parks. In addition, Bedfordshire cycle routes have been marked with signs indicating a number of quiet roads suitable for cycling. These circular routes vary in length from 12 to 25 miles. Off-road cycling – it is difficult to refer to mountain biking in Bedfordshire – is possible at Rowney Warren close to the A600 in a pine plantation owned by the Forestry Commission, and more off-road routes are being developed within Rushmere Country Park.

Living and Working in the Countryside

All of the organisations and facilities listed here encourage the use and understanding of the rural way of life. However, no matter how attractive the countryside may appear, it is lifeless without people. The landscape as we view it today is largely the result of thousands of years of human intervention, so communities working and living in the rural landscape are vital to maintaining a living countryside. This idea has been grasped by policy-makers for some time and one initiative within Bedfordshire is the *Bedfordshire Rural Communities Charity* (BRAC), which is the leading community development agency in the county with a record of over 50 years of activity. The idea is to support rural communities directly, as well as acting as advocates and campaign leaders for rural development.

Successful initiatives have included the Greensand Ridge Rural Development Programme, which was in place for five years and is now anticipating further funding for 2014. Over the previous funding cycle, some £1.4 million was spent on 15 projects across the county. BRAC's portfolio of projects includes assistance with village hall renewal, campaigning for better broadband services and rural transport services, and community-led planning initiatives. The charity also runs an ecological services consultancy. Other interesting areas of support include a farm producing chilli peppers at Chawston, the Warden Abbey vineyard, and the revitalisation of buildings at Ridgmont station to include a tea room and heritage centre.

CHAPTER 10

MUD ON YOUR BOOTS

The starting point for this book was to attempt an accessible guide to the landscapes of Bedfordshire which would increase the enjoyment of anyone interested in the countryside. The intention was not to produce another walking guide, but to encourage those already familiar with Bedfordshire to learn more about the landscape history and, hopefully, to prompt others to explore beyond their regular comfort zone of leisurely strolls. I also had the desire to bring into focus a county which had long been overlooked by many.

A Bedfordshire ramblers group struggles to walk along a greenway which has been damaged by 4×4 vehicles

National guides to the countryside often skip over Bedfordshire, and even specialist publications have found little to remark on. A recent example is a quote from *The Times* in an article by Stephen Anderton covering the reopening of Wrest Park Gardens: 'Pick up the *Good Gardens Guide* or any other mainstream gazetteer and Bedfordshire is always something of a desert...'.

However, during the preparation of the text it became clear that it would be useful to draw attention to some of the best walking routes that provide a flavour of the varied landscapes across the county. There are already a great number and variety of walking guides for Bedfordshire, published as books or single leaflets, and flourishing rambling and walking clubs to tempt anyone outside in both summer and winter. The Further Reading section provides a useful starting point for the best of these, and it would not be sensible to duplicate here this wealth of material, much of which is produced by local groups.

Many of these walks are circular strolls of varying length, beginning and ending in villages and often using a country pub as a reference point. In addition to these circular walks, there are also a number of long-distance paths which transect Bedfordshire. Walking the length of these presents a more formidable challenge and can take on the characteristics of a route march, but the main advantage of these long-distance trails is that they generally follow the grain of the country and reflect the geology – and hence the landscape – of Bedfordshire.

Indeed, the best-known, perhaps, the *Greensand Ridge Walk*, is named after the geological formation which the path follows, for the 40 miles from the Cambridgeshire border in the north-east to Leighton Buzzard in the south-west. While this airy footpath may be the best-known of the long-distance paths, the *Clay Way*, which follows the glacial boulder clay plateau from Cranfield to Bromham for 11.5 miles, is perhaps more characteristic of the walking conditions in the county, with mud underfoot in wetter weather. Therefore, this chapter briefly describes the finest characteristics of these long-distance paths, which can of course be explored in parts or by walking circular loops, without embarking on a major expedition. A brief introduction to these trails helps bring the landscapes described earlier in the book into focus. So we can trace the best walking in the river valleys by following the *Kingfisher Way* as it meanders throughout the Ouse and Ivel Valleys, and begin to appreciate the importance of the chalk uplands, by following the *Icknield Way* as it crosses the Downs.

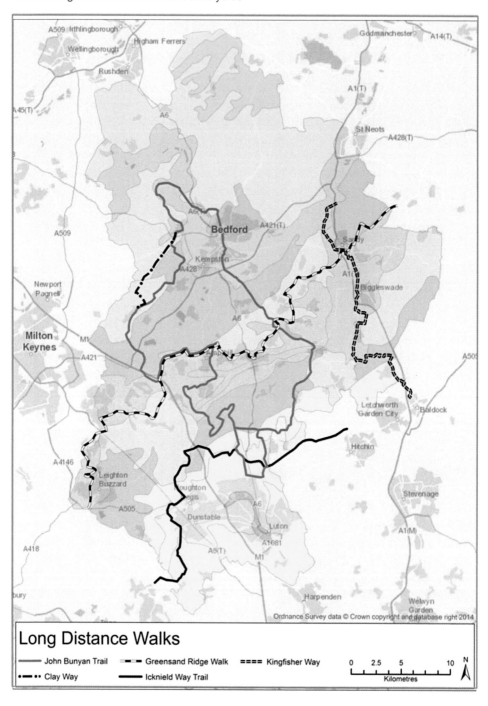

Long Distance Walks

—— John Bunyan Trail   ▪—▪—▪ Greensand Ridge Walk   ▪▪▪▪ Kingfisher Way

•—▪• Clay Way   —— Icknield Way Trail

0   2.5   5   10

Kilometres

N

Ordnance Survey data © Crown copyright and database right 2014

However, we begin with the convoluted *Bunyan Trail* as it weaves a tortuous path around the county for all of 77 miles, crossing all the main landscapes of Bedfordshire and providing any long-distance walker with a stiff challenge. Additionally, there are a few shorter walks utilising the existing network of footpaths, which are of special interest and worth exploring to gain an insight into the varied landscapes of the county.

Use Them or Lose Them: Public Footpaths Belong to the Public

The long-distance trails and paths described in this chapter are part of a national network of walking routes, which criss-cross England and Wales. Many of these, such as the Pennine Way, are internationally famous; others are simply waymarked public footpaths. The Long Distance Walkers Association (www.ldwa.org.uk/) provides guides to many of these paths and, thoughtfully, also funds seats or benches along some paths, especially at points that command a good view. In the county there are estimated to be some 826 miles of public paths, for which Central Bedfordshire Council has responsibility and Bedford Borough has 608 miles. Local authorities take this responsibility seriously, as do ramblers' groups in the county, who have dedicated footpath officers to liaise with local government. An initiative to promote the use and maintenance of footpaths is the Parish Paths Partnership (P3), which aims to improve access to the countryside. Volunteers help to improve paths by replacing stiles, for example, and many produce guides to local walks. Some 60 parishes are involved in Bedfordshire. Some groups have taken the step of publishing information on websites: Arlesey, Linslade Wood, Harlington, Shefford, Stotfold and Studham are examples. Arlesey, for example, gives details of eight walks. Bedford Borough Council has published a 'Rights of Way Improvement Plan: 2012–2017', 'to ensure that the network is improved, marketed and valued as a key public asset'.

The Bunyan Trail (BT)

This long-distance footpath is really a collection of existing paths which have been waymarked to link places throughout Bedfordshire that are connected to John Bunyan, the Puritan evangelist and author of *'Pilgrim's Progress'*. The trail is indicated on waymark posts with a distinctive Bunyan logo. John Bunyan lived in Elstow and travelled extensively on foot, preaching and following his trade as a tinker. He clearly had a keen eye for landscape and when, imprisoned in Bedford for religious reasons, he used his memory of long walks to enliven his writings; the Chilterns were described by Bunyan as the 'delectable mountains'.

The BT utilises existing public footpaths, including long-distance routes such as the Clay Way mentioned above, and coincides with shorter sections of the Greensand Ridge Walk, the Chiltern Way and the Icknield Way. The best way to describe the BT is to say that it meanders; one website reports that the waymarking is 'sporadic in places', and (in common with much of the walking in Bedfordshire) the site also warns that 'parts of the route can be muddy'.

For those interested in landscape, the best approach to this long walk is to consider the Bunyan Trail in two sections: these are well described on the Let's Go! website (www.letsgo.org.uk/walk/TheJohnBunyanTrailPart1.aspx). The exact length of the trail is not clear but the Long Distance Walkers Association (LDWA) confidently reports a measurement of 77.3 miles. It is appropriate to begin at Bunyan's birthplace of Elstow, close to the Moot Hall, and the well-marked trail at this point heads south in a straight line towards Wilstead. Here the trail crosses the well-drained and flat Ouse Valley terraces, which are often gravelly at depth with loam and sandy topsoils. South of Cotton End, however, the trail moves on to land underlain by Oxford Clay, which tends to hold up water and create imperfectly drained areas. This area, once called the Bedfordshire Fens, is now marked by regular deep drainage ditches, which have converted this poorly drained clay land into profitable arable fields. This is truly the 'slough of despond' which would have discouraged Bunyan, and must have been a daunting obstacle to any traveller. However, from this depressing area there is a view south to the edge of the Greensand Ridge, and soon the trail climbs towards the village of Haynes, where Bunyan once held religious meetings. Close to this point, the trail crosses the Greensand Ridge Path. The topography here becomes more broken and wooded and the trail skirts the edge of Rowney Warren Wood, now well used by off-road cyclists who enjoy the sudden slopes and dells of the many dry valleys and the drier conditions formed within the sandstones.

The trail emerges north of Shefford, crossing the valleys of the Flit and Ivel Rivers, again climbing out of the bottom lands onto the glacial boulder clay hills of mid Bedfordshire and meandering through villages such as Meppershall and Shillington, with views south to the edge of the chalk. Here the footpath runs almost due south and comes under the influence of chalk from the nearby escarpment. This land is valuable and mostly arable, based on the chalk marl subsoil, which after ploughing will give a characteristic white or grey tone in the fields. At Hexton the trail is directly under the chalk escarpment and turns west to Barton before climbing onto the chalk escarpment at Barton Hills, adjacent to the attractive parish church with its characteristic flintwork stone facings. North of Luton, the BT, the Icknield Way and the Chiltern Way form a dense network of footpaths across this chalk landscape. Eventually the BT enters the Sundon Hills Country Park where all three long-distance paths converge. This is also a convenient car park.

The BT can also be followed on a much longer leg of some 45 miles from Sundon Hills, leaving the chalk by a dramatic descent from Sharpenhoe Clappers and crossing the flat Gault Clay vale towards Pulloxhill, where the water tower is a good landmark. It takes a long southern loop to reach Harlington, where the life of John Bunyan is recorded by a stained-glass window in the church: it was in Harlington that his prison sentence was passed, sending Bunyan to jail in Bedford.

Crossing the Flit Valley once more, the trial loops back onto the Greensand Ridge around and through Flitwick and Ampthill before reaching Houghton House – Bunyan's 'house beautiful' – giving a superb view to the north across the Marston Vale and Oxford Clays. At this point the trail coincides with the Greensand Ridge Walk, following the scarp west across well-wooded and interesting topography before striking north at Ridgmont, again crossing the Oxford Clays and providing a glimpse of remnants of the former brick-making industry around Brogborough. The trail then climbs the clay ridge at Cranfield joining the Clay Way footpath to give splendid views of the Marston Vale to the east, before crossing the Ouse River terraces at Kempston and looping north following the river to Pavenham.

This section of the walk is characteristic of the Ouse limestone landscape, with villages such as Oakley, Clapham, Stevington and Bromham all on the Ouse terraces. These areas are much favoured by modern housing developments, which in the recent past have encroached onto the flat floodplains. A more cautious approach is now being followed. Finally the trail enters Bedford, passing the prison buildings where Bunyan was held, and re-crosses the Ouse to return to Elstow.

For the diligent and enthusiastic walker with an interest in the landscape, the BT provides a complete introduction to the county – apart from the north Bedfordshire uplands. Some interest in John Bunyan would also be useful. The advantage of this long-distance circular route is that it can be joined at numerous places and the path also passes through numerous villages, crosses Bedford, and skirts the northern edge of Luton. However, it can be difficult to follow in places, and the walking guides provided by the organisations listed in the Further Reading section are invaluable.

The Greensand Ridge Path (GRP)

For any walker in winter, mud is ever present throughout Bedfordshire, except on lengthy stretches of this Ridge walk. As the name implies, the topography is dominated by the Greensand Ridge, which lends itself to excellent walking and provides great views from many points. There is ample variety in the landscape, with pasture, arable fields and horticultural land; older mixed woods and new conifer plantations; parkland landscapes surrounding the great houses such as Woburn; accessible public parks at Ampthill and Rushmere (formerly Stockgrove Country Park); land used for recreation, such as golf courses; numerous Sites of Special Scientific Interest (SSSIs); rare examples of southern England lowland heath; a bird reserve close to Sandy; and even a vineyard.

The variety of the land is partly due to the presence of patches of glacial till which in places overlie the sandstone, resulting in wetter and smoother landscapes in many places. These patches of wetter land are often closely interwoven with the more erodible sandy land, such as at Maulden Wood. The GRP provides an insight into this varied slice of landscape, which has never been as valuable to agriculture as the surrounding clay lands. The topography is broken by steep dry valleys, and soils are often sandy and easily eroded.

The 40-mile GRP can be subdivided into eastern and western sections, with the village of Clophill roughly in the middle. In the east the starting point is actually in Cambridgeshire within the village of Gamlingay. The topographic character of the route is immediately obvious as the path crosses the parkland of Woodbury Hall, one of the many landscaped parklands along the GRP. The place names which include the word 'heath', such as Gamlingay Great Heath and Little Heath Farm, indicate the poor quality of this land historically for agriculture. This characteristic is reinforced as the path joins one of the few Roman roads in the county, which is bounded by an historic feature in the Hasell Hedge, a formidable feature of unknown antiquity.

Approaching Sandy the substantial Sandy Warren (now operated by the RSPB as a reserve) is visible to the south, and the path then crosses the narrow floodplain of the Ivel River and climbs towards the village of Northill. The difficulties of clearing land for arable production along the Ridge has left a legacy in the landscape. Here, the woodland covers a series of ancient fish ponds just south of the path, which were utilised by the monks of a priory at Ickwell Bury, one of several ecclesiastical sites which favoured the Greensand Ridge. This section of the GRP towards the village of Haynes is interesting as the Greensand is masked by a thin but agriculturally important cover of glacial clays. This renders the land more favourable to arable production; the landscape is smoother and fields larger as the path approaches the A600.

At Chicksands, the site of another priory, the GRP crosses the JB trail, and the Greensand path re-enters the sandy broken landscape adjacent to Rowney Warren. This is another typical feature of the Greensand – areas where rabbit warrens were once common in the well-drained sandy soils. Occasionally the rock can be seen in old quarries or cuttings.

At Clophill the now modest River Flit cuts through the Ridge. The dimensions of the gap cut into the Greensand, which is now followed by the A507, suggest this river was once much larger. The strategic nature of the river gap was recognised by the Normans, who left an impressive motte with accompanying well-preserved baileys just south of the village, forcing the main road to make a dangerous bend to avoid the earthworks. The GRP, however, remains north of the Flit Valley and passes through Maulden Wood, which has two designated SSSI sites. The Maulden Wood SSSI is an ancient woodland site situated on a cap of boulder clay where fragments of semi-natural woodland remain within the broad-leaved and coniferous plantation. There are many examples here of ground-cover plants which have survived undisturbed in this old woodland: plants such as the early purple orchid (*Orchis mascula*) and herb paris (*Paris quadrifolia*).

To the south on the Lower Greensand, fragmented areas of the former heath land habitat still exist within plantations of Scots Pine. West of Ampthill the route crosses the well-used Ampthill Great Park, which was formerly a royal hunting reserve, illustrating that the value of this land for recreation was well recognised in the past. The north- and west-facing escarpment provides extensive views across the clay vale to the valley of the Ouse and to the glacial till ridges beyond, and the sense of being above the lowland vales continues as the GRP climbs close to Millbrook golf course and the vehicle proving ground.

Both these areas are typical of the way in which the Ridge, with its varied and often broken topography, provides space for competing land uses, and the path here is shared by walkers, cyclists and horse riders. The large-scale conifer plantings around Millbrook thrive on these sandy soils. Crossing above the M1, the GRP enters a belt of pleasant, lightly wooded land famous for bluebells around the Woburn Estate. The abundance of mixed and conifer woodland in this area is a legacy of the historical interests of the Woburn Estate in managed woodlands, which continues today. The path then enters the main Woburn Estate where the deer herds are an integral part of the parkland landscape.

The creation of this picture-book parkland required the relocation of the village of Woburn (1747–61) when the present Abbey was built in the classical style. West of the village there is more estate woodland before the path crosses the Roman road of Watling Street and enters Rushmere Country Park, which is an ideal point for any walker to join this long-distance footpath. This area around the country park is a microcosm of the landscapes along the Greensand Ridge. The National Nature Reserve at Kings Wood is typical of the mixed and coniferous woodland along the Greensand; close by is heath land at Rammamere; there are the abandoned sand quarries at Fox Corner just outside the park; and a spur of glacial till-covered land at Overend Farm has well-preserved ridge and furrow field patterns created by medieval arable ploughing. Kings Wood, opposite the entrance to the country park, is a National Nature Reserve (NNR) containing the largest area of deciduous woodland in Bedfordshire with a history which can be traced back to before the fifteenth century.

The GRP therefore provides an accessible route across one of the most attractive and varied parts of Bedfordshire. The light, often markedly sandy, soils have resulted in a very mixed pattern of land use which is unusual in the heavily farmed landscapes in the south of England. The mosaic of woodland (both planted conifers and ancient deciduous woods), parkland landscapes and areas of pasture and heath are interspersed with arable land, usually on a thin capping of glacial clay.

Modern access gate on Clay Way, near Cranfield

The Clay Way (CW)

This is one the county's shorter waymarked footpaths, at about 11.5 miles in length, but the attraction of the path is that it commands spectacular views of Marston Vale, the Greensand Ridge and also to the west into Buckinghamshire: the path also links or passes close to many of the most important ancient woodland sites in Bedfordshire. It also provides unobstructed views of the wind farms around Cranfield, which are a modern addition to the landscapes throughout England. However, as the name suggests, this trail is across the glacial boulder clay of the uplands west and north of the Oxford Clays, and it can be wet underfoot. The northern starting point for this interesting linear walk, which can easily be achieved in a day, is at Bromham Mill, where there is car parking. This site has now been restored and hosts a visitor and interpretation centre. The CW climbs out of the Ouse Valley and skirts the edge of Hanger Wood, which is another example of the ancient woodlands so common on clay soils. In this case the main species are oak, with rowan, hornbean and aspen, which allow adequate light to penetrate and encourages woodland flowers in the spring. Much of this area is now within the Forest of Marston Vale, which includes other ancient woodlands such as Marston Thrift: all these woods are carefully managed to gradually restore the mixed tree cover with a ground cover of woodland plants. One special gem along this route is Astey Wood which is carpeted in bluebells in the spring.

The Icknield Way Path (IWP)

Walking in Bedfordshire can be a muddy experience, as the Clay Way and Bunyan Trail illustrate, and it would be easy to conclude that a walk on the edge of the Chilterns chalk would be firmer underfoot. However, the weathering of chalk can also result in sticky clay soils with flint stones embedded, which makes for difficult walking when land has been ploughed; the smooth, springy turf of Dunstable Downs is a more inviting experience for the walker. The Icknield Way is an ancient route which traces the course of prehistoric trackways from the Chilterns into East Anglia, and the tracks are always above the clay plains and provide stunning views to the north. The IWP was opened in 1992, and is the result of a campaign to link ancient trackways across England from the south coast to the Wash. For the ambitious, it is possible to walk from Lyme Regis to Hunstanton on these paths, but locally the 40-mile stretch from the River Ivel at Ickleford in the east, to Ivinghoe Beacon in the west, provides a great walking experience with plenty of interest, and all within the Chilterns Area of Outstanding Natural Beauty (AONB).

From Ickleford, walking westward, the IWP crosses some of the most fertile land in the county where the marl soils abut the formidable chalk escarpment to the south. This fertile land below the Chiltern scarp is derived from the nearby chalk and the soils are loamy, deep and calcareous, with gentle slopes, which make the area good for wheat production. In contrast to the clay plains adjacent, this marl land has the advantage of being accessible in the late autumn when other fields are waterlogged, making winter-sown wheat and oilseed rape popular arable crops. At the village of Pirton the path passes the well-preserved motte and bailey castle known as 'Toot Hill' (meaning 'a look out'), adjacent to the eleventh-century parish church and the site of a now deserted village known as 'the Bury'. Long depressions trace the streets of the former village, and close by are signs of ridge and furrow cultivation.

Fertile marl soils at the edge of the chalk (Wantage series)

This ancient landscape continues with the trackway of Wood Lane which climbs steadily onto the chalk. The IWP then passes the entrance to the NNR of Knocking Knoll, important for open chalk land favourable to butterflies, and then other nature reserves at Deacon and Telegraph Hills. This area is open access land which is maintained by careful management, including traditional sheep pasturing, to encourage chalk-loving plants and prevent scrub encroachment. There is an opportunity at this point to climb Galley and Warden Hills, which are examples of the hard Upper Chalk.

There is a confusing tangle of footpaths close to Luton, with the IWP, the BT and the Chiltern Way all crossing, but the main Icknield Way heads north to the edge of the chalk escarpment at Sharpenhoe Clappers and the Sundon Hills Country Park, where there is ample parking. This area is the highest point in Bedfordshire and the SSSI is representative of chalk grassland habitats. Botanists have always been excited by the flora of these chalk hills and there is a long history of early plant collecting and, more recently, detailed recording of plants in this area and throughout the county.

Naming the Plants: County Vegetation Records of Bedfordshire

County floras have been and still are an important feature of scientific endeavour in England. In Bedfordshire a recently published account follows in a long tradition of such works, from Charles Abbot's Flora Bedfordiensis in 1798 to James Saunders' Field Flowers of Bedfordshire in 1911 and, more recently, John Dony's masterly Flora of Bedfordshire of 1953 and the Bedfordshire Plant Atlas of 1976. The authors of this new publication, Chris Boon for the flowering plants, and Alan Outen for the mosses, have each spent many years studying natural history in the county. Assisted by other naturalists, the book is the culmination of more than 20 years' comprehensive recording in the county. The Flora of Bedfordshire (2012) provides an up-to-date account of the status and distribution of the flowering plants and mosses of the county, and places their occurrence in the context of over 400 years of study of the local flora. A unique feature is the indication on the maps of the distribution data from a survey carried out in the 1970s by John Dony, the distinguished former county botanist, showing clearly the changes that have taken place. For the generalist there are introductory chapters on many aspects pertaining to the flora of the county, including geology, soils, conservation of the countryside and changes in the flora over the last 50 years. It also provides accounts of the history of botany in Bedfordshire, and an overview of the botanical hotspots.

The OS maps record a confusion of different paths all marked as either the Icknield or Chiltern Way as the route crosses the M1 and railway north of Luton: the walker can either tramp north through Toddington and Chalgrave or south through Chalton. This is the most urban part of the path and the true nature of the chalk landscape is best experienced at the Chilterns Gateway Centre on Dunstable Downs where there is again ample car parking. The view from the Gateway Centre – owned by Central Bedfordshire Council and managed by the National Trust – at the summit of the Downs is across the clay plains of Bedfordshire and Buckinghamshire.

The Downs are also designated an SSSI, noted for the quality of their chalk grasslands. Close by are two scheduled and ancient monuments (Five Knolls and Medieval Rabbit Warrens) and there are many other historical features. The chalk grasslands of the Downs have miles of footpaths and several circular walks, a fascinating history, and an abundance of plants and wildlife. From the Downs the IWP can be followed around the enclosure fence of the Whipsnade Zoo and into Dagnall. The path is now on the gentle south-facing dip slope of the Chilterns with arable land growing mostly wheat and oilseed rape, which flourishes on these clay soils over chalk. Much of this land is owned and managed by the National Trust as part of the extensive Ashridge Estate. There are numerous walking paths here leading north to link with the Ridgeway long-distance footpath at Ivinghoe Beacon.

A feature of the Icknield Way is the abundance of archaeological sites close to the elevated edge of the chalk. Maiden Bower, just to the north of the scarp, is an example of a Neolithic causeway camp with clear entranceways and ditches (dating of pottery suggests this site was in use around 3,500 BC), on which site a later Iron Age fort was also built; at Dunstable Downs there is a group of five round Bronze Age barrows excavated by Mortimer Wheeler in the 1920s, which have a long archaeological history from the Neolithic to much later Saxon burials; at Pegston and Deacon Hills there are traces of medieval farming banks or lynchets; and villages such as Pirton have striking motte and bailey keeps from Norman times. These monuments underline the importance of this chalk land close to the north-facing scarp, which was clearly a route into the centre of England, avoiding the wooded and less accessible clay plains below.

> ### *Farming on the Slope: Strip Lynchets on the Chalk*
>
> *A distinctive feature of the steeply sloping chalk escarpment are banks, or terraces, that follow the contour and often occur on the sides of more sheltered valleys. In Bedfordshire, Pegston and Deacon Hills are good examples, as are sites north of Barton and on Badgers Hill near Luton. These features are common on the shallow chalk soils and are created by ploughing on a hillside, thus gradually building a flatter area above to be farmed as a terrace. Early farmers valued this chalk land as it was easily cleared, but any advantage needed to be set against the difficulties of working on a slope and farming a shallow soil. The ridging and terracing of slopes was the answer, and also reduced the danger of soil erosion and any land slippage. Archaeologists now believe that these are Iron Age farming relics with a possible early date of 800 BC, which were sporadically worked until the Middle Ages. The key features of these early 'field systems' are that they are in a strip, along the contour, and enclose a small but precious area of flatter land. Found throughout lowland England, usually on chalk, these fields are similar in chronology to the early square Celtic fields in the western counties of Britain.*

The Kingfisher Way (KW)

Walking alongside a river or a canal is usually seen as the most pleasurable of country strolls: these paths have the advantage of being flat, for a start. However, riverside footpaths often suffer from long detours around private land with privileged riverfront access, or they need to navigate gravel workings, and thread their way through the towns and villages that are sited on floodplains. Following these paths on the OS map alone can be a challenge and on the ground it is often a frustrating experience. However, the major rivers of Bedfordshire have a significant direct impact on the landscape, and the river walks are popular. These valleys provide the routes for communication; flat land along river terraces is competed for by agriculture and house builders; the alluvial land is a common source for gravel extraction; and also provides useful grazing pastures. In the modern era it offers opportunities for recreation, ranging from the proposed international rowing lake east of Bedford, to angling. Following these rivers on foot provides walkers with glimpses of watermills and modern weirs – and the hope of spotting an elusive kingfisher. Otters have returned to some Bedfordshire rivers, but are even harder to spot.

The KW, a distance of 21 miles from Baldock station to Tempsford, makes a brave attempt to allow the walker access to the attractive Ivel and Ouse Valleys with the minimum of disruption. A series of colourful walking leaflets produced by the Ivel and Ouse Countryside Project break this long-distance path into three sections, each a comfortable day's walk. The most impressive feature of this river walk is the presence of long-established agricultural settlement utilising the land and making use of the river for transport. The walk passes some dozen old water mills, there are ancient moated manor houses, such as Astwick Bury,[7] and in 'Stotfold' is preserved a name linked to the lairage of cattle being moved along ancient drove routes. One of these mills, Holme Mill, is headquarters of the nationally known Jordans cereal company and has been restored to become a visitor centre with an adjacent restaurant.

One of the most attractive sections of this walk is at Langford Meadows which, together with Henlow Common, provides some 50 acres of riverside floodplain which are managed for nature conservation. The willow trees in this area are typical of those in the Ivel Valley, and have been managed by pollarding, providing useful timber and fuel. Also the compact nature reserve at the Riddy, close to Sandy, takes its name from a small stream which joins the Ivel and is flanked by flood meadows. The KW ends close to Roxton Lock where walkers can join the Ouse Valley Way, heading eastward along the wider River Ouse.

This walk is difficult to follow along its total length, but is rewarding for the access it provides to these wide river valley landscapes.

And Some Shorter Strolls

The long-distance paths described above provide an insight into the main facets which contribute to the landscapes of Bedfordshire, but it requires a degree of effort to walk through varied terrain. There are also a number of shorter strolls – all of which are well known to local walkers – which can provide interesting insights into the county. If the long-distance paths give an overview of the landscape, then these shorter outings give glimpses of the countryside and its history.

---

[7] The term 'bury' in a place name usually denotes a fortified medieval farm protected by a moat and a lairage is a holding area for animals being walked to market.

Flitwick Manor Park offers a stroll which is a mere mile in length. The park is listed as a Grade II landscape in the English Register of Parks and Gardens, and it preserves many veteran trees, which have survived in a planned landscape. John Thomas Brookes, an enthusiastic horticulturalist and plant collector, added many of the exotic and native trees in an effort to create a private collection of exotic trees and shrubs, including the Bhutan Pine, an Atlas Cedar and a Giant Sequoia as well as impressive Douglas Firs. Access is from a gate at the junction of Church Road and the A5120, west of Flitwick.

The Jurassic Limestone Villages in north Bedfordshire are linked by Bedfordshire's first Geotrail. This walk, beginning at Bromham Mill, strikes north towards Stevington using existing public paths and allows the walker to visit three attractive villages, including Oakley, which have buildings made from the local oolitic limestone. This attractive building stone is formed from ooliths (which are concentric rings of calcium carbonate centred around tiny grains of sand). Stevington has a limestone cross and many houses constructed from the Jurassic limestone. This walk, which is around six miles (if the side trip to Oakley is missed), is described in a Natural England booklet with help from the Bedford and Luton Geology Group (B&LGG) This is available to download from
www.bedfordshiregeologygroup.org.uk/ information.html.

Clophill Motte and Baileys (also known as Cainhoe) commands a vital river gap in the Greensand Ridge where the River Flit has made a distinctive niche in the wooded hills separating Warren and Maulden Woods. Walkers can gain safe access by a footpath from just east of the church in Clophill to the impressive motte, which has two well-preserved enclosed courts (or baileys). Aerial photographs of this site have also shown the presence of numerous earthworks east of the castle mounds, which are thought to be the site of a deserted village connected to the Manor of Cainhoe, on the south of the present main road. The access path from Clophill skirts the now closed quarries which once yielded Fuller's Earth. These now flooded quarry sites are important for wintering wildfowl.

The Sandy Smith Nature Reserve is a dedicated nature reserve now owned and operated by the Greensand Trust. The area, just to the east of Clophill village, was donated to the Trust by a local businessman. The upland part of the reserve is a good example of former arable land on the Greensand which is now being re-colonised by natural vegetation. The lower part of the reserve lies within the Flit Valley where there are some 25 hectares of wet woodland, grazing meadows and reed beds, known locally as the Upper Alders (a County Wildlife Site).

An Insignificant English Parish – a guided walk around Bromham has been documented as part of a Royal Geographic Society initiative to encourage walkers. A series of 'landscape walks' have been identified throughout the UK. This three-mile featured walk, beginning at Bromham Mill, is described in a well-illustrated booklet available to download from www.discoveringbritain.org/. The walk booklet (which is also available in the form of an audio guide) helps the walker to 'read' the landscape. Much of the guide is concerned with the history of Bromham Park.

Walkers are Welcome (WAW) towns – In 2012 Sandy became the first community in Bedfordshire to join 25 other towns around England and be designated a town for walkers.

Details can be found at: www.sandytowncouncil.gov.uk, along with the town's Strategy for Walkers (www.sandytowncouncil.gov.uk/upload/63.pdf) and many local walks beginning in the town.

CHAPTER 11

THE CHANGING COUNTRYSIDE

The problem with predicting the impact of future changes on the landscape in Bedfordshire, or in any other part of England, is the difficulty with perspective. We mostly view the landscape from the window of a passing car or train or, if we are willing to walk, horse ride or cycle, from a public path or bridleway. Viewed from an aircraft, the dimensions change: there is much more countryside than we might think. The villages in Bedfordshire are small and neat groupings of houses: there is more woodland than we appreciate from the ground, and the motorways shrink to narrow ribbons, curving through the landscape.

Harvesting herbs and spices for the Indian restaurant trade in mid Bedfordshire

Bedfordshire does not offer many grand vantage points, but a view from the chalk escarpment or the Greensand Ridge is seldom only of uninterrupted farmland, but of a mosaic of small woods, farmland and villages marked by church towers or the occasional water tower. Overall, agriculture uses about three-quarters of the landscape in England, and in Bedfordshire the proportion is likely to be greater, which amounts to a lot of countryside to be managed by modern farm businesses – which are also the custodians of the environment.

The second perspective is the changes that take place over time. In general, landscapes evolve slowly unless we are thinking of a new road or building project, which can appear very quickly. As mentioned previously, the more radical changes which have shaped what we see today took place over several centuries. Land was enclosed from the open fields over 200 or more years; it took decades before the parkland associated with the great houses began to be accepted as the norm for what we now regard as typical of the English countryside; and it will take time for the tree planting of the past decade to register an impact. In rural Bedfordshire, as throughout the rest of England, everything is older than we think. Also, recent changes in the way land is farmed under various countryside stewardship schemes are not often immediately obvious to the casual observer. When the countryside is being discussed, changes are often posed in terms of a threat, and emotive language such as 'concreting over the English landscape' are frequently used. However, changes that are long-lasting tend to take place slowly.

Throughout this brief guide to one English county, the message has been that the countryside is dynamic – it is under continuous change. The more we understand and value the landscape, the more opportunities will appear to exert influence on the decisions we make, or which are made on our behalf. Change is inevitable but can be steered away from the more unsightly outcomes if approached with a degree of understanding. Therefore, if we are to evaluate the future transformation of Bedfordshire, it is important to understand how the present landscape is shaped and where future change – not always threats – will come from. In his masterly descriptions in *English Landscapes,* W. G. Hoskins writes of landscapes as even more than just scenery. He argues that a landscape can be deciphered like a code and he finishes the introduction to his 1973 book by quoting a lecture by Constable, the great painter of English landscapes: 'We see nothing till we truly understand it'.

Agriculture

The overriding influence on the countryside in Bedfordshire is agricultural. Nationally and internationally, there are clear trends that can be detected which will shape the appearance of the future countryside throughout the UK. In the early 1980s the UK government signalled a move away from the policy of 'food from our own resources', which had shaped agricultural production from the end of the Second World War. This had encouraged the widespread use of fertilisers, the extension of land drainage, the removal of hedgerows, and – above all – high yields. At about the same time, the European Union (EU) also began to reshape the structure of subsidies within the Common Agricultural Policy (CAP). The drive to increase *production* – squeezing as much yield or value as possible from each acre – was to be replaced by a new approach, which was to recognise the *stewardship* responsibilities of the farmer or landowner. Over the next few decades, the removal of direct production subsidies and the move to schemes which improved the environmental health of the land and paid landowners for managing the landscape began to change the way in which farmers and landowners managed the landscape.

There are now a whole range of schemes in place that reward responsible stewardship. To the casual observer these are not immediately obvious. Leaving more space around the field headlands – the marginal strip along a field boundary – thus allowing room for nesting birds close to the hedgerow, is one example. Since 1987 a number of these voluntary agreements have been introduced, which pay farmers to protect or enhance biodiversity, landscape and historic features and also promote public access. These changes and many others take place under agri-environmental agreements and countryside stewardship schemes, in which whole farms are committed to farming in an environmentally sensitive way. It is estimated that some 12 per cent of all farmland in England is working within these schemes. The private sector has also latched on to this movement, with added premiums paid to farmers for operating with environmental concerns in mind. A local example in Bedfordshire is the food processors Jordans of Biggleswade, who ask farmers to supply a *Conservation Grade* for cereals supplied to them. Conservation Grade status promotes the use of land for wildlife as well as grain production, and commits farmers to having a minimum of 15 per cent of their land under conservation management. This initiative requires farmers to farm in a sustainable way, in return for a contracted premium price for their cereals.

Farmers and the Landscape: Payment for Land Stewardship

During 2013 the Common Agricultural Policy (CAP) was revised and details were published in early 2014. This revision was forced on the EU by criticisms of how the CAP was operated. The new format will include a 'Greening Payment', which will be 30 per cent of any funds awarded. This requires maintaining a minimum of 7 per cent of a farm as an 'Ecological Focus Area', which may include afforestation and other environmentally sensitive measures.

The aim of the CAP, when first created, was to provide farmers with a reasonable standard of living, consumers with quality food at fair prices, and to preserve rural heritage. Over the years, the CAP has moved away from traditional subsidies of the past, such as market price support, and come closer to the provision of public goods, particularly environmental benefits, with the rural environment playing an increasing role. It is this aspiration of encouraging farm businesses to contribute to the upkeep of the countryside, now referred to as environmental stewardship, which has the most potential for rural England. Presently there are a number of schemes operated by the UK government through Natural England and funded by the Department of Environment, Food and Rural Affairs (Defra), which provide funding to farmers and other land managers to deliver effective environmental management on their land. These initiatives have already made a considerable impact on the landscape, noticeable, for example, in wider areas of rough grass around arable fields, the planting of trees in field corners, and the planting of hedgerows. At the advanced or higher level of the scheme, there are payments for initiatives to encourage farmland birds, protect archaeological sites and provide opportunities for public education on farming and rural affairs. Presently the environmental stewardship schemes in operation have a tiered approach, with farmers rewarded for initiatives which improve the landscape or wildlife. The average payment for each hectare is around €230 per annum.

The overall commercial trend is towards bigger units of production, and small farms will continue to struggle. In contrast, the rise of 'hobby farms', with one or both wage earners working to enjoy a lifestyle choice, is also predicted to grow. So we may see more alpacas or rare breeds and certainly more horses in the Bedfordshire countryside. Different crops may also be a feature: in the recent past, fields of daffodils which have been used for medicinal preparations have added a rare splash of yellow colour, as has linseed (which has a small blue flower). Other fields rented to entrepreneurs from the Asian sub-continent around Silsoe are used to produce herbs for the Indian restaurant trade, and Christmas trees are a commercial venture on the Greensand Ridge.

Despite these welcome initiatives the question debated in farming circles is: how would the industry survive without any subsidy? At present farmers are paid to protect and enhance the landscape, but this may not always be the case. Market forces may eventually prevail with a rise in commodity prices bringing the concepts of stewardship, and farming in an environmentally sensitive way, into conflict with production and profit. There are clear government signals that the agricultural industry will need to produce more food, and use less water in doing so. At the Oxford Farming Conference in January 2011, the message from the Environment Minister was that Britain must grow more food in a different way to respond to climatic uncertainty and world population increase.

Meanwhile, the price of land continues to rise despite the recession. Farm land is seen as an investment, described on one website as 'Fields of Gold: investors discover a lucrative haven in Britain's farmland'. Prices are tipped to soar to record highs, with claims of a 40 per cent rise in value over a decade. Savills, the largest name in the property business, estimated that a fund of £7.5 billion nationally could be available to buy land: average national prices were reported in January 2014 to have climbed to £6,882 per acre, an 11 per cent increase year on year, or a 210 per cent increase over the past decade (*Guardian,* 17 January 2014). The spike in food prices which occurred internationally in 2008 was a warning that cheap food which is mostly imported may not be around forever. The use in the UK media of political terms such as 'food security', more usually associated with African farmers, is now common.

Trees and the Landscape

One of the most encouraging landscape developments over the past two decades has been the steadily rising area in the UK planted to new forests. Beginning in the 1970s with the memorable slogan of 'plant a tree in '73', the area planted has increased year on year with Community Forests, such as Marston Vale, leading the way. The public have enthusiastically supported this movement, buying into the promise that increased woodland is intrinsically a good thing as it contributes to amenity and recreation values, is a bonus for wildlife, and assists in a small way with combating climate change. Most of the trees planted have been saplings imported from Europe, especially Holland, in large numbers – some two million trees imported into the UK from 2003 to 2010. In many cases these trees were grown from seed collected in England and grown on in the Netherlands.

However, using imported trees is now being criticised, as a rapidly acting fungus has begun to decimate ash trees on the Continent and has now been identified in many English counties, including Bedfordshire. As 5 per cent of trees in England are ash, the loss of this native species would be a devastating blow to the landscape, especially as ash is an important hedgerow tree. This uncomfortable prospect can be confirmed from events in Denmark, where the disease was first recognised in 2002 and has now spread across the country.

Dutch Elm disease, which was first recognised in Hertfordshire in the 1960s, was more or less brought under control in the 1970s but its reappearance in 1973 has been linked to imported logs from North America. Today in the UK there are around 10 separate tree diseases attacking both native and imported species such as larch, oak and chestnut. There is even a disease known only in Argentina that attacks juniper scrub. One explanation for this may be increased climatic stress, but there is wide agreement that the global tree trade (which, until recently, was completely deregulated) is the main culprit.

The Forest of Marston Vale will play a significant role in the amelioration of urban development by providing spaces for wildlife and recreation and contributing to the 'green' infrastructure required by the planners. This concept hinges on the Community Forest, which is described as a wooded framework rather than blanket coverage of trees. Selling this concept to the public has been popular, with messages connecting trees and climatic change, a better environment, public access and participation all proving to be a winning combination. The reliance on imported rootstock for the 'whips' or saplings has, however, led to the acceleration of disease in these new plantings, highlighted by ash dieback, and a more cautious approach has been signalled. In other areas, cooperation with developers has resulted in funds being set aside to plant trees in a neighbourhood which would offset the carbon emissions from a family home for a period of 10 years.

As a counterbalance to these positive developments, there was significant public apprehension that the sale of public land (such as that now managed by the Forestry Commission) would place woodland such as Maulden Wood in danger of having public access to it curtailed. This proposal was defeated nationally but could be revived.

Ash Dieback Damage

The landscape in England has been immeasurably enhanced by the addition of exotic tree species, thanks mainly to Victorian plant collectors: think of the stately Douglas Fir, which graces so many of our parks, or the Sitka Spruce, which is the basis of the mass paper-manufacturing industry. However, these introductions have mainly been grown from seed, in some cases smuggled across borders by intrepid garden enthusiasts in the nineteenth century. The more recent urge to create a new habitat by planting forests as a 'quick fix' has overtaken this longer-term approach, and the *Chalara fraxinea* fungus, which attacks the ash from the leaves to the roots, may be one outcome of this instant forest approach.

The alternative – waiting for forests to be nurtured from indigenous seeds grown on in the UK – is not an easy answer, however, and there is a need for more intelligent woodland management with a greater diversification of species, and a more open-minded approach to locally produced saplings. The impressive response of the public to the creation of new woodlands is a positive outcome, with schools getting involved in planting trees, and helping to inspire the next generation of people to enjoy trees and nature. To lose these supportive future environmentalists would be a blow.

Whatever the answer is, the seriousness of the ash dieback outbreak has made professional foresters, countryside managers and the public pause to consider the best way to approach reforestation. As for the impact of the disease on the Bedfordshire landscape, it will be a decade or more before we can take an objective view. It has taken some 10 years to breed a strain of elm tree that is resistant to Dutch elm disease, and the lesson to learn is that forestry and woodland management are more about the benefits to our grandchildren or great-grandchildren, than to the present generation.

More immediate is the threat to property and the resultant insurance costs.

Housing in the South-East of England

The housing boom which has underwritten the British economy over the past several decades is often explained by the shortage of land, the heavily regulated planning systems, and the difficulties of building on green belt land. Over the past few years the consistent message from the government has been there is a need for more housing, especially in south-east England, and planning systems will need to adjust to accommodate this. The challenge to the planning concept of a green belt is now immediate, driven by the notion that this would facilitate economic growth. The exact housing figures are, at best, targets. Local government has been involved in a number of planning exercises which have included the need to provide more homes, and Bedfordshire is no exception. Indeed, it could be seen as a target area for housing development. An example of the planning documents produced is the *Bedfordshire Countryside Partnership: A Vision for* 2013 (see www.bedsand lutongreeninfrastructure.org).

This document clearly defines a target of 90,600 new homes in the county by 2013. Bedford, Kempston and the Marston Vale are defined as Growth Areas and the first fruits of this would be at the Wixams, with a target of 4,500 new houses. The plan is that 60 per cent of these new-builds would be on brownfield – that is, not on greenfield – locations. There is therefore a significant change to be expected in the countryside around major towns such as Bedford and Luton, and a ribbon of new housing strung along major access roads such as the A507 between Shefford and the A1.

Flood Risk in Bedfordshire

The extensive, widespread and prolonged flooding throughout lowland England in early 2014 has focused attention on a number of issues which have not in the past received much media attention. The reality of climate change is beginning to impact on politicians: a parallel debate is the funding required for flood defences, and finally what can reasonably be protected and at what cost. Bedfordshire has an extensive network of rivers which have historically flooded, but pressure on floodplains, and more building overall, has heightened the risks. However, the main threat seems to be unpredictable changes in climate. Following the extensive flooding experienced nationally in 2007, local authorities were required to prepare a Preliminary Flood Risk Assessment (PFRA) report, by European Directive. This was to identify areas of significant flood risk across England, and aimed at providing a general picture of flood risk from local sources, including flooding from surface water (i.e. excessive rainfall), groundwater, watercourses, ditches and canals. It excluded flood risk from main rivers. Using these criteria, the risks were assessed and mapped, revealing that approximately 16,500 properties across Bedfordshire were estimated to be at risk from flooding to a depth of up to one-third of a metre during a rainfall event with a 1 in 200 annual chance of occurring. This report can be assessed on the Central Bedfordshire Council website, and includes mapping at a small scale.

Infrastructure

One focal point for development is the urban fringe of Bedford around the southern bypass formed by the recent dualling of the A421. This area is located at the intersection of two major transport corridor improvements schemes, with the M1 upgrading now also completed. The Marston Vale Forest Authority has been active in trying to secure land which would be planted as a foothold in this zone of development, creating a 'Green Gateway'. Added to this is the ambitious plan to link the River Ouse and Grand Union Canal by a waterway which would effectively join the Wash to the canal systems of England.

In the south of the county, the linking of the M1 and the A5 to relieve congestion in Dunstable would also improve the road infrastructure. The creation of the *Chalk Arc Partnership* is designed to involve Luton, Dunstable, Houghton Regis and Leighton Buzzard in providing green space for recreation and wildlife protection in this increasingly crowded area.

Soil erosion on Greensand Ridge soils along a farm track near Flitwick

> ### Green Infrastructure
>
> *The planning system which operates in England and Wales is often shrouded in difficult and inaccessible language which discourages public involvement. One term which is now often used is 'green infrastructure', which is no more than the green space left over when development takes place: the parks, nature reserves, public footpaths, bridleways, allotments, sports fields and even cemeteries. In the face of rapid urban development in south Bedfordshire, an ambitious partnership has been created to attempt future planning for green space along the edge of the chalk uplands. This area of some 100 square miles, which is described as the Chalk Arc and which is already home to around 300,000 people, will see the construction of close to 30,000 new houses in the period to 2021. In the north of the county several new initiatives are being planned by the Bedfordshire and Luton Green Infrastructure Consortium. This is a partnership of 27 agencies which have come together to secure green space along an arc joining Luton, Dunstable, Houghton Regis, Leighton Buzzard and Linslade. The Consortium has the resources to fund small initiatives, such as a wildflower meadow at Leighton Buzzard, a community orchard at Leagrave, or the restoration of ponds at Harlington. Grants range from £2,000 to up to £50,000. The most ambitious scheme is to link green spaces by corridors which encourage wildlife. Four such green corridors have been identified in the Leighton and Linslade areas, north Dunstable, south Dunstable and north Luton.*

Recreation and Tourism

Bedfordshire is not Cornwall and is unlikely to become a major tourist attraction. This does not mean it is not attractive, but it could be described as an 'unassuming county' (as in the title of this book). There are international tourist sites, such as at Woburn Abbey, and national attractions, such as Wrest Park and Whipsnade Zoo, and the creation of new attractions will also impact on the countryside, if only locally. On the Greensand Ridge, the completion of a Center Parcs holiday park utilises land that was under forestry.

And Finally

The theme that runs through this text has been that both continuity and change have shaped the landscape in Bedfordshire. The view from that passing car or from a ramble along a public footpath is the product of an evolution over a lengthy time span. At the same time, there are far-reaching changes under way and the brief account above is not meant to be comprehensive: the landscape is not static and change – both rapid and evolutionary – will be working through the countryside in the next decade. In reviewing these initiatives it is difficult to avoid the thought that there is a quiet revolution going on, and we have more opportunities for leisure and access to the countryside than in the past.

Thanks to local governments and ramblers' groups, footpaths are increasingly used and maintained: there is more encouragement to cycle and use bridleways for hacking; new areas to be conserved or at least protected in some way are being defined all the time; farmers are being encouraged to be environmentally sensitive in their use of land; schools are involved at all levels from tree planting to environmental projects; and there are a growing number of specialist groups interested in countryside matters, from bats to badgers. There is a complex web of organisations from big hitters such as the National Trust to tiny but effective parish councils engaged in conservation activities and countryside protection. This is backed up by a robust array of legal protection measures to discourage damaging development. The private sector, especially food producers, has discovered the attraction of a countryside dimension to marketing, and butterflies and bees are in demand to woo consumers.

It is, of course, not all good news. Recent changes in what the government describes as 'the removal of red tape' will make it simpler for land managers to remove hedges. The compensatory planting of new woodlands in field corners and in plantations will not replace the diversity and ecological importance of a long-established hedge. The last audit of farm hedges in 2007 revealed that 16,000 miles of hedges had been removed in the period 1998–2007.

In addition, there will be natural threats to the use of land in the English lowlands. In 2007 large areas of central England experienced severe flooding, mostly from the overtopping of river banks in catchments such as the Avon. This was followed by increased winter rainfall in 2011, throughout 2012, in late 2013, and most dramatically in 2014. Persistent rainfall, coming in prolonged and heavy downpours across wide swathes of lowland England, has raised fundamental policy issues and led to heated debate. These events are predicted to become more common as the climate warms. For the farmer this will make working the land in autumn, which is the preferred time for arable field operations on heavy land, more difficult. Remember, Bedfordshire is a county of clays, and, conversely, on more sandy soils the dangers of soil erosion can also inflict damage during heavy rainstorms.

It is tempting to think that the landscape we all know will prevail and we can relax and take the dog for a walk in the woods. However, this would ignore the one consistent strand running through this account. Change is inevitable: will the farm subsidy regime which favours environmental protection be sustainable if land prices soar and there is mounting pressure to produce food when market prices rise? Will the green belt hold, and can the county accommodate not only the houses required but the infrastructure to support the rising population? What effect will climate change have on agriculture? Wetter winters and hotter summers will change cropping patterns. Finally, and most importantly, will we continue to give priority to keeping Bedfordshire landscapes in good heart and productive?

At the centre of this account has been the contention that if we understand more of the history of our landscape and how we arrived at what we have now in the Bedfordshire countryside, then we can do more to protect it. This is perhaps an aspiration, but at another level it may be that some familiarity with the landscape history can make that walk with the dog, or cycle ride, or even a car journey, across Bedfordshire more interesting. We all enjoy a nice view. The aim of this book has been to look beyond the merely picturesque, and encourage an understanding of how the land is shaped, in the hope that will improve the reader's countryside experience.

*Extraction of Oxford clay from a brick pit in Marston Vale dated May 1929.
The view is of the London Brick and Forders Ltd, Elstow Works.*

FURTHER READING

This chapter is not meant to be an exhaustive reading guide, but is simply to encourage anyone interested in exploring further. Where possible, websites have been provided, with a brief note if required. I have provided publisher names and dates of publication where possible, but for older publications this has not always been possible.

Production of ornamental roses on the Ivel terraces close to Shuttleworth

Bedfordshire History

Peter Bigmore. *The Bedfordshire and Huntingdonshire Landscape.* Hodder & Stoughton, 1979.
Laurence Meynell. *Bedfordshire.* The County Series, 1950.
Joyce Godber. *History of Bedfordshire 1066–1888.* Bedfordshire County Council, 1984.

Landscape History

Edward Thomas. *The Ickneild Way.* Constable & Co., London, 1911.
W. G. Hoskins. *The Making of the English Landscape.* Hodder & Stoughton, 1955 (republished in 1967).
W. G. Hoskins. *English Landscapes.* BBC Publications, 1973.
D. Kennett. *A Portrait of Bedfordshire.* Robert Hale, 1978.
Oliver Rackham. *The History of the Countryside.* J. M. Dent and Sons, 1986.
Oliver Rackham. *Trees and Woodland in the British Landscape.* J. M. Dent and Sons, 1976.
Richard Hartup. *Gold Under Bracken: the Land of Wales.* Ylolfa, 2011.

Stephen Anderton. 'Wrest Park swaggers back its Baroque splendour.' *The Times*, 30 July 2011.
At www.thetimes. co.uk/tto/life/courtsocial/article3109537.ece.
Roy Millward and Adrian Robinson. *Landscapes of Britain.* David & Charles Publishers, 1977.
John Julius Norwich. *A History of England in 100 Places.* John Murray, 2011.

Local Government

The websites for the three local government areas within Bedfordshire (www.bedford.gov.uk, www.centralbedfordshire.gov.uk, www.luton.gov.uk) contain a wealth of information relating to access to the countryside, including footpaths, open access agreements, cycling and countryside sites.

Mapmakers

Betty Chambers. *Thomas Jefferys and his Map of Bedfordshire.* Bedfordshire Historical Society, 1983.

Geology

Geoffrey Cowley. *County Review: Minerals Aspect Report.* Bedfordshire County Council, 1972.

G. D. Nicholls. 'Introduction to the geology of Bedfordshire.' *Journal of the Bedfordshire Natural History Society and Field Club,* vol. 2, pp. 9–16, 1947. Contains a black-and-white map.

Timothy Farewell, Peter Friend, Martin Whiteley and Joanna Zawadzka. *The Mapping of Landscapes, Geology and Soils in Bedfordshire and Cambridgeshire.* Bedfordshire Geology Group, 2011.

The Bedford and Luton Geology Group was established in 2004 and has a useful website. This group has also produced a number of information leaflets on local geological sites of interest, such as the Tiddenfoot quarry (www.bedfordshiregeologygroup.org.uk/ leaflets/RIGSEdTidLedburn.pdf).

Jill Eyers, *The Building Stones of Bedfordshire.* The Bedford and Luton RIGS Group. At www.bedfordshiregeologygroup.org.uk/leaflets/RIGSBuildStones.pdf.

Bedfordshire: A Summary of Mineral Resource Information for Development Plans. Scale 1:100,000. British Geological Survey and Department of the Environment, 1995.

Water Supply

National Rivers Authority. *Groundwater Vulnerability 1: 100,000 Map Series.* Map sheet 31, Bedfordshire, 1995.

British Geological Survey. *Soil and Rock Characteristics above Groundwater:* Map at 1:100,000. Map sheet 7, Bedfordshire, 1988.

Soils [9]

Thomas Batchelor. *General View of The Agriculture Of The County Of Bedford.* Published in London by B. McMillan for Richard Phelps in 1808. This document was drawn up by order of the Board of Agriculture and Internal Improvement. It includes a rare hand-coloured engraved folding frontispiece map and is an important volume in the series of surveys conducted for the Board of Agriculture, containing a detailed account of the Duke of Bedford's innovations and improvements to the Woburn Abbey Estate. A second edition was published in 1813.

---

[9] There is no recent comprehensive survey of the soils of the county, but several area-specific surveys build on earlier work.

T. Rigg. 'The soils and crops of the market garden district of Biggleswade.' *Journal of Agricultural Science*, vol. VII, part IV, 1916. Unfortunately, only very small-scale maps are included.

D. W. King. *Soils of the Luton and Bedford District. A Reconnaissance Survey.* Special Survey No. 1, Soil Survey of England and Wales, 1969. This contains a black-and-white map at the scale of one inch to the mile.

Soils of Bedfordshire I. Sheet TL 14 (Biggleswade). Also contains a 1:25,000 map. 1987.

R. I. Bradley and P. S. Wright. *Soils of the Shuttleworth Estate, Biggleswade, Bedfordshire.* Cranfield University, 1988.

P.S. Wright, Soil Survey Record 112. Soil Survey of England and Wales at Harpenden, 1987.

C. A. H. Hodge, et al. *Soils and their Use in Eastern England.* Soil Survey of England and Wales at Harpenden, 1984.

MySoil. Free app for use on iPhone and iPad. Compiled by NERC, 2014.

Agriculture and Land Classification

General View of the Agriculture of the County of Bedford with Observations on the Means of Improvement. Thomas Stone, 1794. Printed by Hodson, London.

Thomas Batchelor. *General View of the Agriculture of the County of Bedford.* Published by Richard Phillips, London, 1808.

Dudley Stamp. *The Land of Britain: Its Use and Misuse.* Longman, London, 1948.

C. E. Fitchett. *The Land of Britain: Part 55, Bedfordshire.* London, 1943. This complements the publication in 1937 of the one-inch to one-mile scale maps for the county.

Agricultural Land Classification of England and Wales. Report to Accompany Sheet 147, Luton & Bedford, 1969 (accompanied by a map at 1:63,360).

'Wealthy foreigners buy up swaths of UK farmland and country estates.' *The Guardian*, 17 January 2014.

At www.theguardian.com/business/2014/jan/17/foreigners-buy-uk-farmland-estates.

Vegetation

C. Abbot. *Flora Bedfordiensis*. W. Smith, Oxford, 1798.

J. Saunders. *Field Flowers of Bedfordshire*. Eyre and Spottiswoode, London, 1911.

J. G. Dony. *Flora of Bedfordshire*. Luton Museum and Art Gallery, 1953.

J. G. Dony. *The Bedfordshire Plant Atlas*, White Crescent Press, 1976.

C. R. Boon and A. R. Outen. *The Flora of Bedfordshire*. Bedfordshire Natural History Society, 2011.

K. Lambert and A. Gotti. *The Good Gardens Guide.* Reader's Digest, 2012.

Natural History

B. S. Nau, C. R. Boon and J. P. Knowles (eds). *Bedfordshire Wildlife*. Castlemead Publications, 1987.

Conservation Organisations

Bedfordshire Natural History Society. The society exists to study and record landscape and associated wildlife and to encourage others to learn more about the county (www.bnhs.co.uk).

Natural England. Natural England is an executive non-departmental public body responsible to the Secretary of State for Environment, Food and Rural Affairs. Its purpose is to protect and improve England's natural environment and encourage people to enjoy and get involved in their surroundings. Many of the direct influences on the countryside fall within the remit of NE, including the administration of SSSIs, environmental stewardship schemes, open access legislation and National Nature Reserves (NNRs).

The Wildlife Trust. This conservation charity works throughout England and Bedfordshire is grouped with Cambridgeshire, and Northamptonshire. Its website (www.wildlifebcn.org) provides details of sites in Bedfordshire managed by the charity.

The Greensand Trust works in partnership with local organisations to both conserve the land along the Greensand Ridge and to promote a more sustainable future. This work of this charity includes conservation work, the management of sites, promotion of footpaths and environmental education (www.greensandtrust.org).

The National Trust. In Bedfordshire the NT is responsible for Dunstable Downs and the Whipsnade Estate within the Chilterns Area of Outstanding Beauty (AONB).

The Bedfordshire Biodiversity Recording and Monitoring Centre keeps a record of species and maps distributions of plants and animals in the county. It produces an annual report and has access to a library of landscape photographs.

Gardens

The Walled Garden – Luton Hoo. The garden is only open on designated open days. For details, email office@lhwg.org.uk.

Wrest Park Garden. Currently being restored by English Heritage, this extensive garden covers a formative period in the history of English landscape gardens.

Walking Groups

Details of all the walking groups operating in the county can be found at the Ramblers website (www.ramblers.co.uk). The Ivel Valley Walkers is probably the largest of the local walking groups, and organises a variety of rambles of varying length, all year round. Other groups are North Bedfordshire, Leighton Buzzard, Lea and Icknield, and Ouse Valley.

***Himalayan Balsam** (Impatiens glandulifera):*
an introduced plant that has escaped from gardens and is
rapidly colonising river banks and other areas of damp ground.
Photograph taken in the River Flit valley

ACKNOWLEDGEMENTS

The front cover illustration is a detail from a painting by Thomas Fisher entitled, *Flitton Moor: Bedfordshire.* The painting shows peat cutters at work on the moor, which continued as a peat resource until into the early 20th century. The picture is dated to around 1815. This painting is in the care of the Flitwick & District Heritage Group, which kindly gave permission for its use in this book.

The illustration entitled *Map of the Soil of Bedfordshire* is reproduced on page 41. This forms the frontispiece for the 1813 edition of a publication by Thomas Batchelor. This book entitled a, General View of the Agriculture *of Bedford,* was drawn up for the Board of Agriculture and Internal Improvement. A copy of this text is held by the Bedfordshire and Luton Archives and Record Service.

Central Bedfordshire Council, Minerals & Waste Team have kindly given permission for the use the Solid and Drift maps of the County. The aerial view of the Marston Vale brick making site is from the Aerofilms Collection, presently being catalogued by English Heritage. Permission to use this image has been granted. The map showing the distribution of clay soils in Bedfordshire is reproduced with permission of the authors and the publisher Bedfordshire Natural History Society.

Finally I would like to acknowledge the support I have received. My family patiently helped to correct this text, and over the years have listened to long-winded descriptions of soil maps and landscapes. A number of critical but supportive readers, notably Ian Baillie and Bob Jones, have provided technical advice and encouragement. Rhys David and David Jordan, have read and commented on selected chapters. Bob Jones also contributed to the layout of the text. Ian Truckell crafted the graphics that illustrate the landform distribution. Jane Hammett has provided a very professional editing service and much sound advice along the way. Diana Jackson at Eventispress has prepared the manuscript for printing and publication.

However, I remain solely responsible for the content and final presentation. Errors and omissions in the text are mine and I would be happy to receive comments and corrections emailed to wbkerr47@gmail.com.

Brian Kerr , Ampthill, July 2014